GROWING UP WITH

SPACEFLIGHT:

THE SPACE SHUTTLE

To My
NEW PAL
DouG
BEST WISHES

Wes Oleszewski

2/25/2017

Cover design by Wes Oleszewski
Cover photo by Wes Oleszewski and NASA

ISBN: 978-1-942898-07-8

Dedicated to Miles O'Brien, who took me from slob to VIP with just a couple of text messages.

Series edited by
Jim Banke and Pat McCarthy

Some people got to experience America's space program up-close and personal, hands-on, steeped in the excitement of the peaceful advancement of human civilization.

The rest of us had to watch it on TV.

"Everything that we do in our adult life stems from something that we went through in childhood that other people blew off."

- My Mom, November 22nd, 2014

GROWING UP WITH

SPACEFLIGHT: THE SPACE SHUTTLE

THE ALT:
ENTERPRISE- AUGUST 12, 1977

It was just after 11:50 Michigan time on the humid morning of August 12, 1977 as the first Shuttle orbiter ever constructed sailed effortlessly through the sky over Edwards Air Force Base. My eyeballs were glued to my bedroom's TV set and I don't recall breathing during the entire flight. After just over two years without any hint of United States manned spaceflight, the space-buff in me had reawakened. There may even have been a few drops of drool on my bedroom floor in front of where I was seated. I had shut the entire world out as I teleported myself into that chase-plane whose TV camera was capturing the flight. Of course I wasn't really there. You could tell because there were no nose prints on the canopy glass.

Two years earlier, at 5:18 pm Eastern time on July 24, 1975, the Apollo-Soyuz Test Project (ASTP) came to an end when the Apollo Command Module splashed down. Unfortunately, during most of the two years following ASTP, very little was heard as far as progress on NASA's next venture in space, the Space Shuttle, was concerned. Instead the media was garnished with sound bites and brief filler stories where only the Shuttle and space program critics had the stage and danced to the tune of the negativity that was their trademark. Their song was the myth that if the Shuttle was canceled "all of that money" being spent would be sent instead to whatever federal program they favored. Everyone from astronomer and hater of manned spaceflight Carl Sagan to congressional blow-hard William Proxmire got into the act. Indeed all would be right with civilization if only the Space Shuttle were to be cancelled.

However, just a year and a half after the ASTP, the orbiter test bed ENTERPRISE was flying at Edwards AFB on the back of the 747 carrier aircraft. At first, the media did not see this as much of a story, but by August 12, 1977, when the first free flight of the Approach and Landing Tests, (also known in spaceflight speak as "the ALT,") took place the media came back, at least for the moment and so did many folks in America. Coverage began early in the morning and ABC News nearly covered the event from wheels up to wheels stop. After all, the network brass at that moment saw the Shuttle as new and somewhat exciting. TV rating points may be gained. For me, the ALT blended both of my passions: aviation and space. The first ALT free flight took place just 14 days before I left home to attend the Embry-Riddle Aeronautical University in Daytona Beach, Florida to begin my aviation career. Two weeks before I embarked on that adventure I would be introduced to the Space Shuttle and an orbiter by the name of ENTERPRISE.

To me as well as a lot of other space-buffs, somehow the Space Shuttle was pie-in-the-sky compared to what Apollo had been. After all, spaceflight had to be done with giant tall rockets and capsules, didn't it? A big glider that was boosted piggy-back into orbit and then simply sailed back to Earth to land on a runway seemed to be more like science fiction. As far back as Apollo 15, in the summer of 1971, the makers of Tang were running commercials depicting the all fly-back version of the Space Shuttle. They were pressing the official NASA line that the Shuttle would be making its first spaceflights in 1978. Yet to me it all looked like something out of a bad movie about the future. All of that changed for me on the morning of the first ALT flight.

Leading the news on the morning of August 12, 1977, was not the news of the ENTERPRISE and the ALT. Although that was the largest story of the day, the lead story was the fact that the court had ordered New York City's "Son of Sam" serial killer David Berkowitz to undergo psychological evaluation; gee, there's a shocker. Oddly, in that same day's local news, my cousin Paul was also featured because he had served in the Army with Berkowitz. Paul even displayed a baseball glove that the killer had loaned to him, but never reclaimed. The news then went back to national subjects and the ENTERPRISE.

Much to my personal delight all three networks were giving saturation coverage to the ALT in their morning news programs. All three had gotten their star spaceflight anchor crews out to the desert at Edwards Air Force Base to announce the event. CBS had stationed their long time space reporter Morton Dean to sit at a desk in the desert and broadcast the flight, aided by technical advisor Leo Crupp from Rockwell International, which had constructed the ENTERPRISE. Similarly, ABC's Frank Reynolds and Jules Bergman also were in position. NBC, however, came up with a somewhat different angle on coverage. Of course, they had Roy Neal, a veteran TV space reporter who had been covering flights since the first Mercury missions, standing next to what looked like a night-stand that had been "borrowed" from his hotel room. That piece of furniture was now being used to hold up a model of the Shuttle and 747 carrier aircraft. But back in the NBC New York studios they had anchored the coverage with Jack Perkins, aided by a big-screen projection TV and seven "high school science students." The premise being that if the ALT's moment in history was to have any meaning at all, it would have the most meaning for the "youth of America." A valid point considering that most adults in the country at that time were indifferent toward the Space Shuttle program, including those who were running NBC. In the end, after the ENTERPRISE had landed, and Jack Perkins asked what the students thought of the flight. Those "high school science students" mercifully contributed less than a minute of adolescent stammering and interjections that decades later still remain somewhat painful to listen to.

The mechanics of the ALT were fairly straightforward. Using a Boeing 747 aircraft that NASA had purchased from American Airlines and heavily modified to carry Shuttle orbiters on its back, the ENTERPRISE would be taken aloft and then released to glide down and land on the dry lake runway at Edwards. Of course nothing in NASA can ever be that simple. In the case of the ALT a great deal of data was to be obtained and thus a great deal of planning, organization and practice had been involved. There had to be check points and calls in the mission profile to ensure that absolutely everyone was at the exact same point, on the exact page, at the exact same moment. Even this straight forward drop-test would be handled by Mission Control in Houston and thus was treated more like a lunar landing than an unpowered flight test from the Right Stuff days at Edwards.

Aside from the actual flight testing and data crunching, there was also an element of "show" added to the first ALT. NASA had been under fire from the usual gang of spaceflight haters both in the government and in the media. Critics were constantly after NASA to prove that the Shuttle program was "worth it." So, it became important to put the best public face on the ALT. Stylized tents for VIPs were erected where a good view of the runway could be had. Invitations to all sorts of guests who would be spaceflight friendly were sent out and huge numbers of cars and campers were allowed onto the base to witness the event.

(See Image 1, page 74.) ENTERPRISE crewmembers, astronauts Fred Haise, commander; and Gordon Fullerton, pilot; were not allowed to eat breakfast at home and then just come to work at the flight line. Instead they were corralled into a special room adorned with historic aerospace photos and a pot of flowers and made to eat the "astronaut's breakfast" of steak and eggs in front of the cameras. Haise, the spaceflight veteran, just casually jumped through that traditional hoop; Fullerton appeared obviously uncomfortable. Of course the cameras then followed the crew all the way up the mate/de-mate structure's ladder to the ENTERPRISE itself. Again, Haise waved and smiled; Fullerton appeared obviously uncomfortable.

THE ALT:
AN EVOLUTION TO THE ERA OF LIMITS

NASA had the high hopes that this fairly simple mission would place a successful face on the Space Shuttle and that it would at least mute the critics for a short time. As the morning news shows signed off they announced their times for the start of their ALT coverage. Although the 747 Shuttle Carrier Aircraft (SCA) would release brakes for takeoff at 11:00 in the morning Eastern Time, the actual separation of the orbiter was planned for 45 to 50 minutes later. Thus, CBS and NBC would start their coverage at 11:30. ABC, however, would be starting their coverage with the SCA's takeoff at 11:00. So I sat in my basement bedroom and glued myself to the local ABC station; WJRT channel 12 in Flint, Michigan. Cable TV was still five years into the future for my little farm town community of Freeland and I was forced to use an antenna to snag the signals out of the air. How primitive!

One of the little lesser-known facts about the departure of the SCA and ENTERPRISE is that when Haise and Fullerton were sitting in the cockpit, they could not see any hint of the huge 747 that was carrying them.

"It was kind of like riding a magic carpet ride," Haise would later recall "You're just moving along the ground and then you take off."

Following the takeoff of the SCA and ENTERPRISE,

the networks had little to do other than "fill" because the picture that was being broadcast from a NASA T-38 chase plane was simply the SCA, the orbiter and the other chase planes with blue sky and clouds as a backdrop. Thus there were clips of the "new" Shuttle EVA space suit, the "rescue ball" for emergency crew transfer, and the launch manifest. That manifest, it was said, would one day achieve 56 Shuttle flights per year. And finally there was the new type of astronauts called "Mission Specialists." The jobs speculated for the Shuttle included building a solar power station in orbit that could beam back energy and one day provide as much as 25% of America's electrical energy. Then there was the building of a space station to provide a permanent presence in space. Of course, only half of those predictions ever came true. ABC even filled several minutes with clips from "Buck Rogers," "Star Trek" and the hit movie of the summer of 1977: "Star Wars."

There also were the interviews with the politicians who were on hand to watch the event. Foremost among them was California Governor Jerry Brown. He had joined the 1976 presidential race on the motto that the United States was entering an "era of limits." That tag line became his campaign motto as he lost in the primaries to Jimmy Carter, who then took on the same motto to a somewhat lesser degree. When Brown failed to be nominated, he held on to his "era of limits" ideal and took it with him back to California. The problem was that an era of limits directly conflicted with the concept of a Space Shuttle. Reporters were keen to stick a microphone in Brown's face and pose that question. Considering that billions dollars in Space Shuttle funding were being sent to California and that state was set to hugely benefit from the program, the reporters were in the hope that Brown would squirm. Yet Brown, the pure politician, simply circle talked and turned the question on its heels.

Brown said that the Shuttle was, "…marking an evolution in the era of limits. The planet is limited and that's why it's so important that we expand beyond."

Fortunately, Brown was speaking far from the ENTERPRISE's touchdown zone, because if the aircraft had gotten some of that greasy slick stuff that he was spewing on its main landing gear it may have slid off the end of the 15,000 foot runway, or even off of the seven-mile-long dry lake.

THE ALT:
GO FOR SEP.

While the mission climbed toward its designated release altitude, I am sure that most folks who were not directly involved with the Shuttle program had little clue as to just how complex the orbiter's systems were. In Apollo, both the Lunar Module and the Command Module had computers to support their share of functions. Those computers combined had less computing power than a common calculator that grade school kids would carry in their backpacks 35 years later. The ENTERPRISE, however, had a set of five computers, four of which worked as redundant units controlling nearly every aspect of the vehicle. Yet a safe landing could be made with just one computer. The fifth computer acted as a back-up in case something happened to the four primary units. The orbiter's fly-by-wire system that manipulated the aerodynamic control surfaces completely depended on those computers. In 1977, the use of computers to completely control anything, let alone a flight vehicle, was close to science fiction.

Reaching their pre-release altitude of 26,500 feet the SCA and orbiter were placed on their launch heading. At the controls of the 747, designated "905," was the most experienced drop pilot on the planet: Fitz Fulton. Acting as his "co-pilot" was Tom McMurtry, who, with flight engineers Lou Guidry and Vic Horton, made up the rest of the crew. At the designated moment Fulton would "push over" into an eight degree dive and once the speed of 270 knots was reached the ENTERPRISE would be released by Fred Haise. CAPCOM "Bo" Bobco in Houston was working the flight with the ENTERPRISE crew with a snap and manner that made you think the vehicle really was coming back from space. Haise and Fulton, however, could not avoid a bit of Edwards test flight banter.

"Thanks for the lift, Fitz," Haise casually quipped.

"You bet," Fulton replied, "any time."

Finally, the crew aboard 905 counted down the final seconds to pushover. They called the maneuver.

"Houston copies pushover," Bobco dutifully replied.

Upon reaching 270 knots in the eight degree descent, Fulton called "Launch ready." Almost simultaneously Haise hit the button and fired a series of explosive bolts that held the ENTERPRISE to the SCA. Separation took place at 22,800 feet; slightly higher than planned.

(See Image 2, page 74.) At the moment of separation, Fulton pulled 905's throttles to flight idle and opened the speed brakes while banking. Aboard the ENTERPRISE, Haise was holding in a five degree, nose-up attitude command. The two aircraft cleared one another nicely.

Also at the instant of separation, however, the orbiter's Master Alarm went off. One of the four main computers, General Purpose Computer (GPC) number two, had dropped off line. Fullerton went through the procedure to isolate that GPC and the flight continued. This failure was later traced to a crack in a poorly soldered joint on the "queue" circuit board. The result was that the manufacturing method used to build those boards was later changed, as was the inspection process. Then all orbiters had their computers retro-fitted with boards made with the new process.

Haise's first maneuver was to conduct a "practice landing" at altitude. In other words he put the orbiter into something similar to a pre-flare attitude and checked its handling. It handled fine, but on my TV set at home I kept hearing Haise and Fullerton talk about a "sideways lurch" being there. The "lurch" was the result of the pilots being seated substantially above the orbiter's center of roll axes, as well as the short wingspan of the vehicle. When a roll input was placed into the controls, the nimble orbiter snapped into the roll and the seated pilots, rather than feeling rotation, instead felt as if they were being tossed sideways.

So sure were the engineers that this lurching event would be present that NASA had special vertical stabilizers added under the Shuttle Training Aircraft's (STA) wings to help simulate the lurch. The STA was a modified Gulfstream II corporate jet whose controls and airframe had been altered to allow it to approach like a Shuttle orbiter. (See Image 3, page 74.)

Flying the ENTERPRISE, the crew found that the orbiter controlled very well. The orbiter was pitched down to an attitude that would maintain 207 knots of airspeed. Although the vehicle's tail cone allowed it to pitch down less than the -22 degrees that would be needed for orbiters returning from space, the descent was still plenty steep. Haise quipped that it flew better than the STA. Houston, however, thought that they spotted a discrepancy. It was reported to the crew that it looked to Mission Control as if the ENTERPRISE's lift to drag ratio (L/D) was "perhaps" slightly low, meaning the ENTERPRISE could come up short of the runway. Haise was cleared to start his base leg turn early to correct the problem. Fullerton, who was then at the controls, began the base turn, but Haise slowed him down. Eyeballing out the window and checking his own instruments, Haise knew that Houston was wrong and they were in fact high on the L/D. When he passed that thought to Mission Control, they replied with an order to apply 30% speed brakes. Apparently, they saw that Haise was correct. A heartbeat later, Houston recommended 50% speed brakes. Houston's misevaluation about the L/D and the early start of the base leg had added a bit of energy to the ENTERPRISE's flight path.

Haise had plenty of landing surface to aim at on the dry lakebed; in the neighborhood of seven miles worth. The little added energy did not bother him at all. He simply lined up and guided the ENTERPRISE down. Per the flight plan, the speed brakes were retracted at 2,000 feet above the ground as Fullerton armed the landing gear. Exactly 1,100 feet later, Haise entered into the pre-flare and raised the nose up from the dive-bomber descent to an easy -1.5 degrees, and at an airspeed of 270 knots Haise commanded the gear down. Fullerton simultaneously pushed the landing gear deployment button. Planned gear-down speed had been 250 knots, but considering that Haise had picked up some extra energy in Houston's botched L/D call, he used the gear deploy as an approved method for scrubbing off speed. The landing gear fully deployed at 265 knots, prompting its three cockpit indicators to go from a tiger-tail indication to the "DN" indication. Unexpectedly, there was no sound heard in the cockpit when the landing gear deployed, but the chase planes confirmed what the gear indicators had read. Haise guided the ENTERPRISE gently toward the runway, and with a bit of float, caused by the excess energy, the orbiter settled gently onto the runway.

I sat there stunned, gazing at my TV set with my mouth

hanging open. The Shuttle was REAL. The darned thing could really fly like an airplane! It was the most fantastic thing I had seen in spaceflight since Conrad and Kerwin had deployed the SAS wing on Skylab. Yet some in the mass media had a different outlook on the ALT. After all it had not flown like pair of pliers, as some had predicted, and there had been no spectacular crash, or unforeseen emergency. So the if-it-bleeds-it-leads news media simply began to shrug the day's event off. Closing out his 26 minutes of live coverage on NBC, Jack Perkins finished with his mumbling group of "high school science students" and, in a hollow attempt to link the ALT to current pop-culture and the red-hot movie "Star Wars," he looked into the camera and said that this means that,

"...today we're a little closer to Wookies than we were yesterday."

It was the most moronic statement made that day-including the babble from NBC's high school science students.

Famed radio broadcaster Paul Harvey led his daily "News" broadcast with the flight of the ENTERPRISE and then in the same breath stated that this day was also the one in which,

"...a man in Oklahoma set a world record by throwing a cow chip 179 feet."

So it was that August 12, 1977, would pass into the pages of history with the headlines of the day documenting a mass-murderer, the ALT and cow chip throwing.

At the time of the ALT missions, NASA's Public Affairs Office had told the news media that they predicted the first Shuttle launch could take place in "the spring of 1979," two years after the first ALT. Watching the event, it struck me that I would be down in Florida getting my degree in aviation during that time. NASA also predicted that flight rates would eventually reach more than one launch per week! Surely I would be there to witness some of that myself. It was a very exciting thought. Of course neither the folks in the news media, nor myself bothered to talk about that 1979 date with the folks at the National Space Technology Laboratory (later know as the Stennis Space Center) who were testing the Space Shuttle Main Engines (SSME) during that time period. The SSMEs would not be de-bugged and flight capable at 100% rated thrust until the spring of 1980, and would not be flight ready at 104% until early 1981.

I also had no idea that the ENTERPRISE herself was far from being an orbital vehicle. In fact, she was in reality little more than an engineering test bed. Her SSMEs and RCS engines were mock-ups, as was her thermal protection system. Her mid-deck did not exist and there was no plumbing for operational SSMEs. Fiberglass made up a good deal of her components as well as her Orbital Maneuvering System pods. She was more of a flying mock-up than an actual orbiter. Yet, sitting there in Michigan that August morning in 1977, and watching the ENTERPRISE fly that first ALT, I was blissfully unaware of any of those shortcomings. All I saw was the future for me and the future for America's space program. I immediately set to work building a small balsawood flying model of the EN-TERPRISE. In a way, it became a metaphor for both my dreams of my immediate future in aviation and for the Shuttle program itself. That is because when it was done, I stored it in the hanging ceiling of my basement bedroom as I shipped off to college; over the years mice dragged it off into a corner and chewed it to pieces.

THE ALT:
LANDING A CESSNA ON THE
SHUTTLE RUNWAY

Although much of America once again rapidly lost interest in the ALT flights after that first test drop, I carried my interest with me onto the Embry-Riddle Aeronautical University's campus in Daytona Beach, Florida. Suddenly I found myself among a whole crowd of people who were just as crazy about flying and space as I was. ERAU was monikered to be "The Harvard of the Sky" although I thought of it as the institution for the aviation incurable. My younger brother put it best when the family dropped me off at school by saying, "It's like he's finally been institutionalized."

Being that Daytona was so close to "The Cape" meant a lot of trouble for a space-buff, as it could easily distract from my required studies. On campus the talk was constant concerning the Shuttle and the remaining ALT missions. All you had to do in class was ask about a term related to the flights of the ENTERPRISE, such as L/D for example, and the instructor would stop everything and enter into an in-depth open discussion on the subject. The library was filled with NASA reports, and as each of the latest reports was published our little library had it. We sat over meals in the University Center and talked about stability and control of the orbiter as if talking about sports. Of course, if you mentioned Star Wars in there anyplace the whole discussion was shot to hell.

Following that first flight of the ENTERPRISE there were four additional ALT flights. The second flight took place on September 13, and was crewed by Joe Engle flying as CDR and Dick Truly as PLT. Unlike the first ALT, there was no live news coverage for the second flight; there was only a brief segment on the network evening news. Likewise the third ALT, which took place on September 23, with the crew of Haise and Fullerton became little more than a footnote in the news media. October 12 saw the first flight of an orbiter in the actual return-from-orbit configuration. This time Engle and Truly flew the ENTERPRISE without its aerodynamic tail cone. At least that flight gained a mention on the evening news, but little else was reported. There is little doubt that the astronauts themselves were happy to see the media spotlight on the ALT fade. They could now simply go to work and fly without the "show" taking place.

On October 26, 1977, some degree of media attention was cast upon the fifth and final ALT, and most of that was a bit unwelcome. That flight uncovered a flaw in the fly-by-wire control system. As Fred Haise and Gordon Fullerton approached the touchdown point, Haise made some corrective inputs into his hand controller, but the ENTERPRISE appeared to wobble, then touch the runway and balloon back into the air where it stabilized and then settled back onto the runway. It appeared to be a classic case of Pilot Induced Oscillation (PIO), but in fact it was anything but classic; it was a unique problem in the fly-by-wire system of the ENTERPRISE. As beginning pilots, we Embry-Riddle freshmen discussed this landing at length, because we were familiar with PIO first-hand. Of course, Haise's PIO was not a product of his error like ours were, but rather had its roots in the complexity of the ENTER-PRISE's control system.

In the ENTERPRISE's control system, commands from the pilot's hand controller were first sent to the General Purpose Computer, evaluated and scheduled out to the aerodynamic control surfaces. The pilot's commands were obeyed in a fraction of a second, but the computer kept the orbiter within the vehicle's limits while doing so. On the final approach that led to the PIO, Haise commanded slight rolls while at the same time commanding nose pitch movements, a normal and reflexive move for a pilot at that point. The two near instantaneous commands went to the computer, which was programmed to give priority to pitch commands, and to limit the rates at which the vehicle's control surfaces could respond. In other words it would hold back some signals while allowing what it was programmed to see as more important signals to pass all at a given rate, or "rate limiting." Then when two important signals had been fed at the proper rate, it let go with the other signals whose rate would also be limited, but whose totality would not. The result was that there was a sort of build-up and lag in the controls followed by an unexpectedly large response. If the pilot then responds to that result, the problem amplifies. Haise was smarter than the computer and simply allowed the ENTERPRISE's oscillation to dampen out through the vehicle's own positive dynamic stability. Later, the problem of orbiter PIO tendency was studied well into the 1980s, but prior to the first orbital flight of the Shuttle, engineers developed "PIO suppression filters" for the orbiter COLUMBIA.

Long after the ALT flights had been completed, we talked about the Shuttle at Embry-Riddle. It was a favored topic during meals. Eventually, however, I decided to put my space nuttiness on the back burner as best as I was able and focus as much as I could on becoming a professional aviator. Still, it was not easy. During the late 1970s a lot of work leading toward the Shuttle was going on. The 15,000 foot long Shuttle Runway had been constructed and actually had an active control tower. Unfortunately, the guys in the tower had almost nothing to do in the late 1970s. Thus, in those days, you could call them up on the tower frequency listed on the sectional navigation chart and request a touch-and-go. They were always more than happy to grant that request. So it was that as a student pilot on one of my flights with an instructor I landed a Cessna 172 on the Shuttle runway.

Compared to other runways I had landed on, including Daytona Beach International Airport where the university was located, the Shuttle runway was far different. First of all it was so darned long that it gave you the illusion that you were far lower than you actually were, so you had a tendency to want to flare too high. Then once you touched down you saw how heavily grooved the surface was. For a little Cessna, it was like landing on a washboard. Looking ahead you could not see the opposite end of the runway, it simply bent down over the horizon with the curvature of the earth. Then as you took off, climbed out and turned crosswind, you could see that your landing had taken up just a fraction of the runway length! Yet, for a guy who grew up with spaceflight, it was a real thrill and it was also difficult to focus on flying and not do any sight-seeing. The VAB was close by and the LUT and "Milk Stool" from the Skylab and ASTP Saturn IBs was still standing tall. Just a couple of years later, however, such a touch and go would have been unthinkable for a student pilot and his instructor in a Cessna. ERAU did not restrict the activity until late 1979 and that was said to be simply because the heavily grooved Shuttle runway was chewing up the tires on the school's fleet of aircraft.

On the 24th day of March, 1979, the Shuttle runway received its first orbiter when the COLUMBIA arrived from Palmdale, California. Three of us drove down to the Space Coast from ERAU together and parked across the river to watch the 747 with the orbiter aboard come in and land. From across the river, they looked great, like a majestic preface to the future in space. Later, on the evening news, the story appeared quite different. Of the 38,000 tiles in the vehicle's thermal protection system, only 60% had been installed, and of those nearly a thousand had come off on the flight to KSC. The up-close images looked far worse than what we saw from Titusville.

(See Image 4, page 75.) Two months later the ENTER-PRISE herself came to Florida and a lot of us made the pilgrimage to the Kennedy Space Center to take the bus tour and see her being test-fitted on Pad 39A. Meanwhile, along the crawlerway and over by the VAB, the number 2 and 3 Apollo Launch Umbilical Towers were being cut up. Large sections of the launch towers had already been re-planted at pads 39 A and B to act as the Shuttle's Fixed Service Structures, but the portions not serving as such were sold for scrap. The number 1 launch tower, with its "Milk Stool" for adaptation of the Saturn IB, was sitting behind the VAB, un-used. It would remain there for several years, serving somewhat as a reminder of Apollo.

For the next year-and-a-half, the work on the Shuttle would be intense and completely behind the scenes. Even the most rabid of space-buffs would hear very little about the Shuttle, and at KSC the bus tours would see a lot of weeds growing where fantastic things once happened. The vast majority of Americans would focus on much more important things… like disco, The Dukes of Hazard and the growing tally of days that the US hostages had been held in Iran.

STS-1:
GETTING RESTED AT MR. DOUGHNUT

My focus in the autumn of 1980 was on my critical role in the advancement of human civilization by stocking shelves and ringing up prescriptions in the pharmacy and cosmetics department of the Daytona Kmart store. This was part of my effort to not only get back into college after having run out of money and gone deeply in debt to the university; it also was an effort to somehow feed myself. Where was Sally Struthers when I needed her?

It was a bitter cold Monday across Florida on the 29th day of December, 1980, as the first operational Space Shuttle stack rolled out of the VAB. At the same time I was rolling a big metal cart of shampoo, denture cream and glycerin suppositories out of the stockroom at Kmart. In the store's appliance department, the TVs showed clips of the rollout on the local central Florida news networks. Oddly, those same news networks completely ignored my rollout of shampoo, denture cream and glycerin suppositories. It seemed, however, that the rest of America ignored both events alike. The stack for Space Transportation System-1 (STS-1) resided on pad 39A for nearly two more months until February 20, 1981, when the Flight Readiness Firing (FRF) took place. In that test the Shuttle's main engines were fired for 20 seconds at 100% thrust while the stack remained held to the pad. The noise not only woke up central Florida, but it woke up the nation. The vehicle was alive!

A month and seven days following the FRF, NASA announced officially that the launch date for the first Space Shuttle would be April 10, 1981. Standing there in the Kmart cosmetics department I decided that I was not going to miss it. I told Andy the pharmacist that I was gonna be down there to see it. Andy asked what I was going to do if I could not get the day off?

"I'll quit the job," I replied

Knowing I only had a bicycle for my personal transportation he asked, "How're you gonna get down there?"

I answered that if I could not get a ride, I would ride my bicycle and get as far south as I could. He just shook his head and snickered. The fact was that I had spent nearly my whole life passionately following spaceflight and nearly every bit of that had been sitting in front of a TV set. There was no way I was going to be this close to that piece of spaceflight history and again have to watch it on TV. I was going to be THERE to witness it first hand, even if I had to ride my bicycle. The only problem was that the best eyewitness location for the launch was almost 50 miles away, a bit longer than the distance I usually rode my bicycle.

As luck would have it, launch day for STS-1 happened to fall on my day off, so now my only problem was getting down to the Space Coast. A day before the launch I ventured to the Avion student newspaper office on Embry-Riddle's campus, and was told that AIAA was chartering two buses to go from the campus to KSC for the launch of STS-1. I hustled down to buy a ticket, but found that the tickets had sold out almost immediately. Dejected, I returned to the newspaper office and began to plot my bicycle ride down US1 to Titusville. I figured it would take me most of the night to get down there, and although riding a bicycle down US1 in the middle of the night to see a space launch may seem a bit nuts, the term "A bit nuts" is denoted on my birth certificate.

Just as I was about to head out and start peddling, my girlfriend of that time stopped me and said that she knew of two guys in her dorm who were driving down. She suggested that we should go to their room and she could introduce me to them. If they had an extra seat, it may keep me from becoming a road pizza on US1. As it turned out the two guys were happy to have me ride along. They were, in fact, both space-buffs just like me and we instantly became friends. Jennings, who owned the land-boat of a car that we drove down in, was from Michigan, just like me, and to this day I consider him to be a good friend. Brian, the other guy, was an expert in everything that flies, and would go on to not only work at the National Air and Space Museum as a photo archivist as well as becoming the author of a most comprehensive book on rockets and missiles, but would also serve as the best man in my wedding seven years later. Together, the three of us headed out that Thursday evening to witness aviation history… or so we thought.

On the trip down toward the launch site we chattered about spaceflight history. Then, as we came within a dozen miles of Titusville, we suddenly saw spaceflight history. Above the trees the darkness was slashed by the crossed white beams of the pad spotlights. Although we could not yet see the shuttle, it was an image that we had always seen in books, magazines and on television. In spite of yourself, it made your heart stop and your jaw drop.

Entering the town of Titusville we suddenly discovered that we had no idea where the hell we were going. Where would we park? What about private property? Collectively we decided just to turn toward the river. Driving down Grace Street we hit Riverview and the riverbank itself. For a few minutes we cruised up and down Riverview calculating a good place to park. I spotted a county pumping station and suggested we should park near it. That way if any of the locals gave us a hard time, we could just go onto county property. We pulled in, bailed out of the car and just stood there frozen by the sight of the white Space Shuttle bathed in those crossed spotlight beams. For a moment, all three of us were kids again gazing at the wonder of spaceflight.

Snapping out of the Shuttle's spell for a moment, I saw that it was just after 10 pm and I decided to hike up Grace Street to the Mister Doughnut shop up on US1. There I found a pay phone and I called my folks up in Michigan to ask "Guess where I am tonight?" Being the parents of a rabid space-buff, it was an easy guess for them. When I returned to the car I was amazed to see that in the past 20 minutes, nearly every parking spot along the riverbank near us had been taken, and there were more cars coming. Clearly, there would be no problems with the local residents tonight.

Opening the trunk of his car, the guy who had parked right next to us, revealed a sort of mobile Space Shuttle flight-following station. Attached to the underside of the trunk lid he had a poster depicting each phase of the STS-1 flight profile. He had charts and table that listed each mission event, as well as assorted abort profiles and abort destinations. He had Shuttle cut-away diagrams that detailed every component. Most importantly, however, he had a small portable TV that ran off of his car battery. In 1981 such TVs were not rare, but in our present location his TV was the center of attention.

Several hours into the night I decided to go for a walk

up US1 and see what may be happening. The streets were busy as I strolled along, and every sign that could have its letters rearranged had a Shuttle best wishes message. After about a mile or so I came upon the local mall. Even though it was the middle of the night, the parking lot was filled as if it were the day before Christmas. The doors to the mall were propped open and people were coming and going. I went inside and was amazed to see that many of the stores were open and doing a good amount of business. Most noticeable was the local toy store which had set up a table just outside of their door. Upon the table was a cash register and stacks of Space Shuttle models which were apparently selling like crazy.

When I got back to the riverbank everyone was standing around gazing at the distant Shuttle or talking spaceflight. We talked about every aspect of spaceflight past, present and future. Most of us simply agreed that we had no idea as to what STS-1 would do, or what the Shuttle's future would really be. It was like going to a space-buff convention. There was, however, only one problem with our space-buff paradise: access to a bathroom. On a later trip up the road to buy a cup of tea I found out that the guy running the Mister Doughnut shop up on US1 did not mind folks using his restrooms, as long as they bought a doughnut "or somethin." When I got back to the riverbank I spread the word and soon folks were strolling up the road to Mister Doughnut and returning "rested" with coffee, or a pastry, or both in hand. STS-1 was already helping the local economy, and the guy running the doughnut shop could testify to that.

STS-1
I'M GONNA STRANGLE JULES BERGMAN

Shortly after dawn the countdown hit the first in a series of holds. The TV in our little mobile Space Shuttle flight following station seemed to pick up the local ABC station the best, so we were glued to Jules Bergman and Gene Cernan. The issues started with a fuel cell problem and then a problem with the back-up computer. The guys on the TV knew about as much about the problems as we did, but Bergman kept down-talking the prospect of a launch today. As countdown recycles and holds folded up on one another, Bergman kept talking about NASA officials stating things such as their "…expectation of having to go through multiple launch attempts over several days."

It was bad enough waiting out the assorted re-cycles in the countdown, but Bergman simply intensified our frustration. We had never seen anything like the Shuttle and at the time of STS-1 we had no idea just how dependant COLUMBIA was on its computers. This was 1981 and desktop computers were just coming out of the "Basic" and "DOS" era. Talk of a misplaced bit or bite gumming up a spacecraft's launch seemed quite strange. In fact two days later we would be told that a simple timing error of 40 milliseconds between the four primary computers aboard COLUMBIA and the vehicle's back-up computer was the cause of the problem. It was easily solved the day following the first launch attempt by shutting everything down and restarting the system. That simple re-boot, however, could not be done at the point in the count where we were on Friday morning. So, we were stuck with Bergman throwing the cold water of truth on our protracted hopes for a Friday launch.

"I'm about ready to swim across the river," Jennings growled, "and strangle Jules Bergman."

(See Image 5, page 75.) Of course, Bergman was correct in one sense. We were not going to see the Space Shuttle fly today.

Over on NBC, the ever spaceflight-dense Robert Bazell was interviewing Jim Lovell concerning problems in space.

"What was the worst kind of problem that you ever had?" Bazell asked the Apollo 13 commander.

Across the nation every space-buff watching NBC must have chuckled and said, "What!? Is he kidding? He's asking the commander of Apollo 13 what was the worst problem he ever had?" The laughter must have lightened up the on-going holds and delays.

Since we were watching ABC I missed out on that little meat-puppet moment until it was on the internet decades later. Finally, after what seemed like an entire day of holds and recycles, the word came across the loop that they were going to once again recycle to T-20 minutes and go out and remove the crew. Some two-and-one-half-hours after the scheduled launch time, the effort came to a halt. Shortly after that came the official scrub announcement. Frankly, it was almost a relief. We had all been awake for more than 24 hours and other than a bag of doughnuts that I'd retrieved from Mister Doughnut, none of us had eaten. Everyone up and down the riverbank agreed to meet in the same place Saturday night for Sunday morning's attempt at a launch.

The next day at work I went into the personnel manager's office and told her that although I was scheduled to work on Sunday, I would be at the Shuttle launch and if it was late, I would be late too. Unexpectedly, she simply smiled sweetly and said,

"No problem, I understand, have fun."

It's funny how folks who live in central Florida have a different view of spaceflight than other people around the country. Of course, most of the country had watched the whole scrub live on TV and from the White House to my parent's house every American seemed to suffer through the recycles with us. Most of them, however, were much closer to a restroom than those of us on the riverbank.

STS-1:
THE DREAM IS ALIVE AGAIN

On the night before the second launch attempt we got a later start out of Daytona than we had the first time. We stopped and ate and this time we were all armed with sleeping bags. Just as we had planned Friday morning, almost everyone parked where they had been for the scrub. This time, however, some of us crawled into our sleeping bags and grabbed a few hours of sleep. I have to admit that I kept waking up, looking at the Shuttle in the spotlights and then covering back up thinking "Wow, this is so cool." I would run through my mind all of the other manned launches that I had watched on TV and remembering how much I always wanted to be where I was at this moment.

(See Image 6, page 75.) As dawn broke folks began milling around again. This time there as a different feeling in the air. I had a sense that the Shuttle was gonna go today. There was an exhilaration among the crowd rather than anticipation, as if we all had our fingers poised on some sort of launch button and were certainly going to push it. A few hucksters were walking up and down the crowd, just as they had done on the day of the scrub, trying to sell assorted souvenirs. One guy had a simple black and white bumper-sticker that had a rough Shuttle image on it and the words "I SAW IT." Someone, I believe it may have been Jennings, shouted to him,

"What if it blows up?"

Without missing a beat the huckster reached into his pocket and pulled out a large black marker. He pointed to an open space on the right hand corner of the bumper-sticker and he said,

"Then you take this marker and over here you write BLOW UP."

He was apparently a huckster with the Right Stuff.

Our friend with the mobile Space Shuttle flight following station in the trunk of his car had taken his place right next to us again. Just like on scrub day, I had remembered to bring along my tape recorder. I'd been taping manned launch broadcasts from the TV since I was 13 years old and had recorded Apollo 14, so I was determined to get this one too. I asked our pal with the battery powered TV if I could place my tape recorder next to his TV at launch time and pick up some of the broadcast. He happily agreed and we all waited as the countdown passed every milestone that it had stumbled upon during the first launch attempt. No one knew what to expect. In fact, the damned thing just might blow up.

We saw nothing but a silhouette of the Shuttle and Pad 39A as the sun came up. It was a bit hazy and so our view remained that of a silhouette against a stunning orange sky while the count ticked down. Like expectant parents we paced a bit and alternated between looking at the pad in the distance and focusing on the little TV set. I kept running through my mind the fact that this was indeed history that could be considered on the scale of witnessing Freedom 7, or Friendship 7, or Gemini 3, or Apollo 8 or perhaps even Apollo 11. Countless space firsts were about to take place right in front of our eyes. I just had to hope that I would not forget to turn on my tape recorder.

As the countdown hit the two minute mark I hit the record button and set the tape recorder down next to the TV. Oddly, about that same time no one was looking at the TV set, every eye that had a view of the pad was focused toward the silhouette of the Shuttle backed by the now amber sky. Everything seemed to get quite still. For the first time there was very little talking among all of us on that riverbank- it was as if we all collectively held our breath.

At main engine start we saw the silhouette of the steam cloud billowing from the engines working against the sound suppression water. Six seconds later the solids lit and we saw what looked like a second sunrise. Then the STS-1 stood up on two stilts of flame as bright as the sun. Everyone was screaming "GO!... Go Baby GO!... GO!" I heard myself screaming it and I heard it echoing up and down the riverbank. What I did not hear, was the Shuttle. Then I remembered something I read in Mike Collins' book "Carrying the Fire." He described watching the first Saturn V, Apollo 4, launch. Collins wrote that about the time he said to himself "You can't hear it," the sound hit him. And just as I had that thought, the sound hit us.

(See Image 7, page 76.) Although there were certainly a few Saturn V veterans present, most folks who were there to witness STS-1 had never experienced anything like the Shuttle. It reached out, took hold of you and shook your senses as well as the ground under our feet. My tape recorder picked up the sound of the items in the trunk of the car rattling. The only thing louder was the sound of the shouts, screams, squeals and rebel yells coming from the crowd. People were jumping up and down and punching their fists into the air as STS-1 ripped into the sky. You really had to work to hear any of the calls coming from Mission Control. The whole thing kept going for over two minutes and then we heard the "Go for SRB sep." call. It was then that everything seemed to grow comparatively quiet with just a smattering of "Hoots" and "Whoooos." A few seconds later at SRB separation we saw the translucent white plume and then saw the two solids dropping away. At that moment a spontaneous cheer went up followed by a rolling applause produced by the near million or so people who now lined the riverbank as far as the eye could see. It was as if the home team had made a fantastically great play in front of a sellout crowd. It was sudden and it was contagious. I found myself clapping as if someone in NASA could actually hear me. That applause was actually captured on my tape. We applauded NASA, the Shuttle and our nation.

Following SRB separation we turned our attention to the tiny TV set once more, watching and listening as STS-1 headed for its target in orbit. In the distance out over the Atlantic the vehicle looked like a very bright star hanging in the sky. As the boost continued we had the illusion that the vehicle was actually heading downward toward the horizon, because that was what it was actually doing. Soon the star simply faded into a pinpoint. A glance at the TV and then a look back toward the sky found the Shuttle lost to the eye. At Main Engine Cutoff (MECO) everyone seemed to snap back to reality.

There was pure joy in the crowd and you heard a lot of "Man! Did you see that?" as if someone there could have missed it. We patted one another on the back, smiled and felt great, even though we had done nothing more than be there and watch. Even complete strangers found one another, smiled gleefully and offered congratulations on a great launch. One fellow coined it all when he grinned widely and said,

"Gee… I wish they had another one."

Even the ride home was conducted as a festive traffic jam. People were filled with pride, and in our car the clogged roadway simply gave us more time to chatter about the launch.

I got back to Kmart in time to start my Sunday shift on schedule. Over in the appliance department a small crowd had gathered around the TV sets. One of guys working in that department had thought ahead and set one of the VCRs to record the launch which was playing over and over again as customers stood and watched, over and over again. On that Sunday the folks that I worked with all heard that I had been there and the guys in the appliance department told their customers,

"The guy over there in cosmetics was down there for it," and pointed toward me.

As I stocked my shampoo, denture cream and glycerin suppositories, dozens of people came up to me and asked "How was it?"

The best I could do was to simply reply that it was inde-scribable and urge them to go down and see one.

For myself, I simply went about my mindless job with a perpetual smile upon my face. After 31 United States manned space launches, all of which I witnessed on TV while growing up with spaceflight, I finally got to be "there" and "see one!" Nearly a million other people who had crowded the length of the Space Coast that morning were thinking that same thought at that same time. Best of all was the feeling that after more than five years without the ability to launch humans into space, our country was finally back in the manned spaceflight business. It was the most exhilarat-ing feeling of my life up to that point, and I could not wait to see the next Shuttle launch. The dream was alive again.

STS-1:
ZIPPER EFFECTS, TEAL, AND AOS

For the next two days we saw live TV from space and clips on the evening news as astronauts John Young and Bob Crippen sailed overhead in COLUMBIA. Huge concern had developed on the first day because when the cargo bay doors were opened, areas on the Orbital Maneuvering System (OMS) pods where found to be missing a few tiles, and that image was shown, live, on the TV. Speculation immediately broke out among the media that this could mean that other tiles had also been lost. The famed "zipper effect," where one tile falls off and a string of tiles behind it follows like a big zipper, was the subject of much speculation. This came primarily from those who pretty much had zero engineering experience and had never witnessed, first-hand, the densification and application of a single tile. Yet "the zipper effect" was a very catchy term that the average slob in his living room could easily relate to, so the media just loved saying it. Unfortunately, the best that NASA officials could do was to restate their confidence, explain that the missing tiles were in a non-critical area and restate that this vehicle had never been flown before.

Later in the flight, Young and Crippen received a phone call from Vice President George Bush. He was speaking in place of President Reagan, who was still recovering from a gunshot wound received in an assassination attempt. The Vice President commented that the flight of STS-1 was just the forerunner of great things to come. Indeed, that was the feeling at that time; good things were ahead and the Shuttle was a good example of that. All they had to do now was return to Earth alive.

Fanning the flames of concern regarding the tiles, the news media managed to find a spark, but not in the area they had expected. Early Tuesday morning, just hours before the Shuttle COLUMBIA was due to reenter, ABC news broke the story that "...super long-range telescopes belonging to the Air Force have confirmed that all of the underside tiles are in place." Then they switched to a feature story on the facilities that they said were called "Teal Blue" and "Teal Amber." The report stated that the Air Force was not at all happy with this information getting out and then, of course, ABC went on to detail the system. Reportedly there were two ground imaging facilities. Teal Blue atop Mt. Haleakala in Hawaii and Teal Amber was in Malabar, Florida. These systems used what ABC remedially called "compensated imaging." In other words they optically compensated for the natural distortions in the assorted layers of the Earth's atmosphere in order to get a very clear picture of an object in space.

ABC went on to report that this highly classified system, which had been used for more than a decade to study Soviet spacecraft and satellites, had also been used in the spring of 1973 to assess the damaged Skylab workshop. It was said that you could actually count the rivets on the workshop which was 270 miles above the earth. Decades later, however, amateur black-project buffs found evidence that the Skylab portion of the report was incorrect. ABC also reported that the secret system could see Soviet cosmonauts space walking. Their source reportedly stated that, "It's just like being there." NASA, dutifully denied that they had such imaging to prove that the tiles were intact. Many years later, the amateur black-project researchers published information that ABC News had been correct, and Teal Blue and Teal Amber had indeed photographed the bottom of COLUMBIA and confirmed to NASA that the tiles were all in place. Ironically, 22 years later a hand full of stubborn, myopic NASA managers would insist that the use of such military assets were, "not required" to evaluate possible damage to COLUMBIA's left wing's leading edge, and by that they would seal the fate of the crew, the orbiter and the Space Shuttle program itself.

In advance of COLUMBIA's return, I had managed to swap shifts around and get the morning off so that I could be home to see the landing. The expected landing time was 1:20 in the afternoon and I calculated that I had just enough time to see the Shuttle touchdown and roll to a stop. Then I would have to get on my bicycle and head for Kmart at a fairly brisk pace. After all, there were cosmetics, vitamins and laxatives to be stocked. This was Florida; people needed that stuff, especially the laxatives.

STS-1:
WHEELS STOP ON THE
COLUMBIA. WHEELS STOP!

Jules Bergman said several times that John Young had told him that the mission would be considered a success if they could get it up, get the doors open, get the doors closed and get it back down again. By Monday they had accomplished exactly half of those goals. Now, on Tuesday, it was time to finish the mission. In these early Shuttle missions communications with an orbiting vehicle were very different from what they would become in the years ahead. "COMM," as it was called in space program speak, was accomplished by way of ground stations, many of which had been established back in the days of the Mercury Program. Thus, they had COMM for a few minutes here and a few minutes there, intermixed with long periods of silence. Additionally, there was the well-known "black-out" period during reentry, which had been experienced in every manned spaceflight. Years later the establishment of the Tracking and Data Relay Satellites, or TDRS, allowed full-time COMM including during reentry. In 1981, however, the world watched the mission, yet we were often in the dark.

TV coverage of the landing began at 10 am Eastern Time, three-and-one-half-hours prior to the scheduled landing time. A two-minute-and-27-second firing of the

OMS engines slowed COLUMBIA enough to allow it to drop from orbit. Just over 22 minutes later, the shuttle went into the reentry black-out. For what seemed like hours, yet actually lasted only minutes, the world waited; some expecting the worst, the rest of us just sat there expecting.

To those of us with a space-buff's ear, the term "AOS" was heard from PAO in the background, and we knew that the vehicle had come through reentry just fine. A few moments later John Young's matter-of-fact voice came through the COMM as if being transmitted from the simulator instead of from the actual mission.

"Hello there Houston… COLUMBIA's here."

I cannot say that I was relieved when those first words out of black-out came across, rather I was reassured. I was reassured that once again those space program critics and Shuttle critics were wrong. Those who almost wishfully hyperbolized the issue of the tiles and who parroted the fabled zipper effect had been silenced, at least for this mission. Now COLUMBIA was making the transition from spacecraft into an aircraft; the world's largest, fastest and heaviest glider.

Everyone in our crummy house full of college guys was, perhaps for the first time ever, silent, as our attention was glued to the TV set. Long range cameras at Anderson Field in California picked up the tiny white speck of an image at just over 200,000 feet in altitude, 340 nautical miles out, moving at Mach 9.6. As NASA's PAO read off the altitudes it was clear that COLUMBIA was eating up the distance at an amazing rate. The camera looking into Mission Control was centered on CAPCOM Joe Allen. Behind him in a very relaxed posture were Joe Engle and Dick Truly, the crew of the next mission. Repeatedly, Allen read off the plot lines and reported to the crew that their course, speed and altitude were exactly as planned. Soon the Shuttle showed up on our TV screens looking like an orbiter rather than a speck. Out of 50,000 feet COLUMBIA dropped below Mach 1, and for the first time a reentering Shuttle's twin sonic booms were heard on the ground at the Edwards Air Force Base landing site.

Lining up with the runway's centerline and glide-slope the Shuttle was joined by the T-38 chase planes, one of which was equipped with a live TV camera. The rest of the way down we all rode along with the Shuttle while it headed toward the runway. As John Young transitioned from steep approach to the pre-flare, I figured that they had it made as long as the landing gear deployed. Just like during the first ALT mission, I don't recall breathing during most of the approach. When that gear came down there was a cheer that came from the TV set! Apparently many of the news people had been holding their breath as well.

"It's incredible, it looks like Los Angeles Airport!" NBC's normally reserved anchorman John Chancellor exclaimed when the orbiter leveled out, "It's perfect and he's coming home from space!"

Just as sweet as can be, Young set the main wheels onto the dry lakebed and then lowered the nose wheel. Kicking up a cloud of dust behind her, COLUMBIA rolled down the runway.

NBC's Tom Brokaw with a tremor in his voice tried to add commentary,

"He's got all the wheels down and he's rolling."

John Young, on the roll, asked, "You want us to take it up to the hangar, Joe?"

"We're gonna dust it off first." CAPCOM Joe Allen replied without missing a beat.

"This is the world's greatest all-electric flyin' machine,"

Young commented as the COLUMBIA slowed, "I'll tell ya' that, it was super."

"Convoy 1…" a voice broke the static, "Wheels stop on the COLUMBIA. Wheels stop!"

(See Image 8, page 76.) The entire nation seemed to take a deep breath of pride. We had been told for years that we were now a can't-do country. Politicians from 1975 to 1980 told us that our country was in an "era of limits" and they fostered the attitude that we need not try to do great things. Our enemies chanted that Vietnam made us weak and we were evil, wasteful and would fail in everything we attempted. America, it was said, was on the decline and we deserved it. This new Shuttle thing was too complex, it would not work because Americans had built it, and everything we touched failed. But when the wheels stopped on the COLUMBIA, Americans could look back at all of that and say "WRONG!" We "can do," we "will do" and we "did do" were now our boasts. The "era of limits" was nothing more than a handy political catch-phrase, a myth; the Space Shuttle was a reality. In the pre-launch words of President Reagan, "Once again we all feel as giants."

On CBS, Dan Rather had the best advice, "Let's just take a deep breath and just… soak up this moment."

That was it, they did it; they really did it! America was back in the manned space arena. It was all I could allow myself to hear and think at that instant. Now I had to wheel my bicycle out the front door of the house and head off to earn my minimum wage at Kmart. All the way there I thought about what had just happened during the past few days. This was a new machine that did amazing things and the plan was to have many, many more of these flights. I wondered how many more I would get to see – provided, of course, that someone driving down Mason Avenue in

Daytona Beach didn't run me over on my way to work today… or tomorrow, or the next day. That's the way a bicycle rider's mind works.

STS-2:
JOE, HENRY… I CAN'T SEE A DAMN THING

It was the final day of the STS-2 flight and I was parked in front of my portable TV in my camo-pants and a T-shirt with something comical written on it as I awaited the reentry and landing of the COLUMBIA. Although I had earlier skillfully managed to swap my shifts around at my universally vital job of stocking shelves at the Kmart cosmetics and pharmacy department in order to be home for the scheduled STS-2 landing, the shortened mission could easily have foiled my plan. Of course I would have developed a reason to call in "sick" in such a circumstance. I would have had a vision problem; can't see going to work when there is a Shuttle landing on TV. As it turned out, such drastic measures were not required because the second landing of COLUMBIA would take place on my scheduled day off. Thus, the laxatives, vitamins and zit creams would be fully stocked by some other slob and the time and space continuum would remain in its proper order. Plus I would get to record the reentry and landing. It is hard to break the old habits of someone who has grown up with spaceflight.

As they prepared for de-orbit, Engle and Truly found that their low-sleep, high-work scheme kluged to optimize their shortened mission was beginning to catch up to them; both men were fairly fatigued. To make matters worse, a failed fuel cell aboard COLUMBIA had an unexpected consequence as well. Fuel cells combine hydrogen and oxygen to chemically produce electricity. A useful by-product of that action is pure water. However, in the failed unit aboard STS-2 a membrane in the fuel cell had leaked hydrogen into the spacecraft's drinking water. This meant that the water was filled with tiny bubbles of hydrogen which, in micro gravity, remain suspended rather than bubbling to the surface and expiring. When a person drinks that water they take in the hydrogen gas, which eventually results in a reflexive burp that is accompanied by the expelling of some of the water. Engle and Truly quickly decided to simply avoid drinking the water. For that reason both crewmen were not only tired, but also dehydrated at the most critical phase of the mission.

Knowing that the mission was being compressed and not wanting to waste a moment on the chance of becoming motion sick, Dick Truly had applied a scopolamine patch to himself earlier in the flight. Just prior to reentry, he replaced that patch with a fresh one to protect him from any vertigo in the reentry phase. During the set of critical manual maneuvers, Truly's job was to read from a cue card and remind Engle of the details of each maneuver as they reentered. Engle was supposed to hand-fly the orbiter all the to the ground as a part of their mission's testing. The atmosphere in the orbiter's cockpit, however, was very dry and both astronauts were rubbing their eyes a lot. Truly, unfortunately and unknowingly, had some residual scopolamine contaminating his fingers. What neither of the crewmen knew at that time was that scopolamine will dilate your eyes. Engle later recalled that,

"I'd pitched (the orbiter) around and was about ready for the first maneuver and said, 'Okay, Dick, let me make sure we got the first one right,' and I read off the conditions.

I didn't hear anything back, and I looked over and Dick had the checklist and he was going back and forth and he said, "Joe, Henry and I can't see a damn thing."

It was not the best situation for the two astronauts who were about to try and guide the most complex flying machine ever constructed back into the earth's atmosphere by hand-flying it.

STS-2:
A WELL SQUISHED PEANUT
BUTTER SANDWICH

Prior to their launch in the second week of November, 1981, excitement concerning STS-2, the second launch of America's Space Shuttle, was at a similar pitch to STS-1. Yet that excitement came with a different tone. Now, although most of America and indeed most of the world knew that there was a Space Shuttle, most folks still didn't really know how it worked or what it was all about. Still its existence had permeated into the public mindset. Nearly half a year after the launch of the first Space Shuttle, the roar of the SRBs and main engines on the Space Transportation System had awakened the nation, but Americans still weren't quite sure what they were looking at. Now, NASA was preparing to give the public another lesson.

Launch day found me on a bus headed from the Embry-Riddle Aeronautical University's Daytona Beach campus to KSC. Unlike STS-1, this time I actually managed to find a seat on the bus. So, instead of being 14 miles from the pad I would be standing on the causeway about 8 miles from complex 39A. Just the prospect of being that much closer to a Shuttle launch was exciting on its own merit. As our bus exited I-95 in the predawn darkness there was an atmosphere of confusion surrounding the launch time. Earlier the previous day there had been a failure of a multiplexer aboard the orbiter and there was talk of a launch delay. The news media of the day had not quite evolved to the point of 24/7 coverage. Thus, most of us were left with whatever reports had been on the 11 o'clock news the night before. Even those were highly sketchy, some saying that the unit had been repaired others saying the new unit was being flown in from California. Of course everyone on the bus was of the same mind-set as me and none of us were going to take a chance on missing a launch, so we all piled on the bus anyway and headed for KSC.

For most of us, this was the second time around for this whole "bus to KSC to see STS-2 launch" exercise. Originally, STS-2 had been scheduled to launch some six days earlier. At that time the countdown had gotten as far as T-31 seconds and then cut off at auto sequence start. The cutoff was caused by a high temperature in one of the Auxiliary Power Units (APU) that was sensed by the sequencer. This event had been caused by clogged oil filters in that APU and the entire launch ended up being scrubbed. We had all spent an uncomfortably cold Florida morning walking around the causeway and listening closely to the loop on small loudspeakers strung along the waterfront. It had been a misadventure where a long night turned into a disappointing morning for most folks at KSC. For me, however, any chance to get on to KSC and get close to Launch Complex 39 was a plus.

I spent a lot of those pre-dawn hours gazing over toward the ITL. Having been constructed in 1964, the ITL was the Integrate, Transfer, Launch complex for the Air Force's Titan IIIC booster. From 1965 until 1992 Titan III vehicles were stacked and launched at the ITL lifting off from either of Pad 40 or 41. They were then replaced by the Titan 4, IVB and 34. Some of the most secret cargoes ever flown from American soil departed by way of the ITL aboard the Titan IIIC. There were two original high-rise buildings, the Vertical Integration Building (VIB) and the Solid Motor Assembly Building (SMAB) that always dominated the ITL. Each building had a series of narrow frosted windows to allow the sun in. At night those windows seemed to glow a subdued greenish blue and when you looked at them you just knew that something really secret was going on inside. As of this writing the ITL no longer exists and Pads 40 and 41 are used by SpaceX and ULA. Only the SMAB remains standing and it still has those windows.

A week after the scrub, as our bus inched its way toward KSC, word came from a local radio station that the troubled component aboard the orbiter that had caused all of the doubt the night before had been replaced. The downside was that there would now be a delay of several hours in the launch. Considering that our bus was in traffic so thick that we had actually been passed by an armadillo on the roadside, we all saw the delay as a very good sign. At least it would give us time to get to the causeway and get off the bus before the launch.

Turning onto the NASA causeway our bus was stopped by a KSC official. Some brief conversation took place between the official and our bus driver, then the bus made of 180° turn and started heading back. Just as we were about to panic the bus driver came over the PA system. He explained that he had been told that there was no more room for buses on the causeway and instead we were being rerouted to view the launch from the VIP site. A cheer went up!

Doubling back about a quarter mile we came upon a two lane road that led north toward complex 39. Called "Static Test Road" this easily-overlooked little roadway led to another small road off to our right. That golf club shaped drive looped around and allowed our bus plus another dozen or so other buses to stop and unload. Although we were only about three-quarters of a mile closer to the pad now than we were at the causeway, it seemed to us as if we were right on top of Pad 39A. We were told that our location was called "bunker number 7." Actually it really wasn't much more than a cul-de-sac cleared of the Florida undergrowth that had once been used for tracking cameras. There was, however, a small set of bleachers constructed at the south end and that was already filled with the real "VIPs" who had arrived earlier.

I guess the term "VIPs" was only being used in the general sense here because those of us on the buses who were the causeway overflow mixed quite easily with these folks. Most of them were friends of families of crews, contractors or spaceflight workers. As the crowd grew, our "VIP" area began to load up with spectators of all sorts. Everyone went looking for a good place to sit on the ground, yet still be able to stand up and take pictures of the launch. Scouting around quickly, my Avion newspaper buddy "Cheff Spaghetti" and I saw one large open area that seemed to have a perfect view. We both commented that we could not figure out why no one had staked out this area and we headed over there and planted our butts on the ground. It took about 15 seconds before we realized exactly why no one else had taken the spot. You see, it takes about 15 seconds before the first couple of fire ants from the nest you're sitting on start to sting you. Leaping to our feet we bounded out of there sweeping away fire ants as we went. We spent a good part of the rest of the morning watching that spot and snickering as other people made the exact same mistake.

Of course no VIP site is complete unless it has some extension of the KSC gift shop to take money from the VIPs in exchange for assorted souvenirs. Bunker number 7 was no exception to this rule. Indeed, a small portable gift trailer had been set up and was doing a good business. They probably would have gotten every dime that I had if I would have had a dime. Unfortunately, all that I had was my camera, my tape recorder, my thermos of hot tea and a fairly well-squished peanut butter sandwich with really cheap strawberry preserves on it. In my college days I formed a strange habit that I still retain to this day, which is traveling around without as much as a penny in my pocket. This was due to the fact that I was a starving college guy trying to work my way through school, so I was normally without ready cash anyway. Later in the morning I was sitting for a short time in the bleachers when one of the real VIPs sat down beside me and showed me an STS-2 postal cover. She told me they were selling them at the gift trailer for $1.75 and that you could have them officially stamped and even mailed off at the postal trailer. Looking at the covers I told her,

"That's really cool."

She suggested that I should buy one and mail it off to my folks. I chuckled and replied that the only problem was that I didn't have $1.75. She looked at me a bit surprised, than I explained that I was working my way through college by way of Kmart. Sympathetic she asked,

"Well… didn't you bring anything with you?"

"Yeah," I said as I reached into my backpack and showed her my well-squished peanut butter sandwich with really cheap strawberry preserves on it.

She laughed and handed me one of her postal covers with orders to take it and send it to my folks, adding that she fully understood about working your way through college. She even pulled a couple of postage stamps from her purse and gave them to me. Pointing at the cover she said,

"One day, that'll be a collector's item."

Inside the cover was a small note-card sized sheet that was blank on one side and gave some common Space Shuttle facts on the other side. I took a moment to scribble a note to my folks on the blank side also denoting that the countdown was currently at T-2:00:08 and counting. Dropping the note card into the cover I happily trotted to the portable post office near the gift shop trailer and mailed the envelope that one day may become "... a collector's item."

STS-2
T-31 SECONDS AND COUNTING

Joe Engle and Dick Truly were strapped aboard the COLUMBIA at about the same time that I dropped my collector's item cover into the mailbox. To most of the public they were unknown rookies who had never flown before in space, but to us spaceflight buffs these two pilots were far from being rookies. Engle, in fact, was already an astronaut who had flown in space before he joined NASA. He had flown the X-15 a total of 16 times between 1963 and 1965, with three of those missions reaching altitudes above 50 miles. This qualified him to wear astronaut wings. Additionally, Engle and Truly actually had a "one up" on the first Shuttle crew of Young and Crippen. To date Young and Crippen had performed one landing of a Shuttle orbiter, but the crew of Engle and Truly had already performed two landings of a Shuttle order. In 1977, Engle and Truly were two of the four pilots who flew the Space Shuttle Approach and Landing Tests with the orbiter ENTERPRISE.

Glued to assorted portable radios we monitored the count as it was broadcast by various local news stations. When the count neared the planned time to come out of the scheduled T-9:00 minute hold, Launch Director George Page elected to take a moment before resuming the count. It was his intention to keep his controllers cool, take a deep breath and make sure they were doing everything right.

That little bit of extra hold time, however, really annoyed some of the newsmen. Anchorman Frank Reynolds on ABC TV complained that all along we had been told that everything was going so smoothly, and now THIS! His technical advisors tried their best to explain that this was simply a "take a breath" extension of the hold, but Frank was still a bit disgruntled by the few extra moments in the hold. Of course that media banter meant nothing to the launch director. After just a few short minutes the count resumed and the COLUMBIA again had the undivided attention of millions of people around the world.

After the previous week's scrub nearly everyone seemed to be hypersensitive to the T-31 second mark in the count. As that point came and went a cheer and applause echoed through the crowd. Apparently everyone seemed to have the perception that if you got past that moment in the count you were good to go. In fact, I noticed for many years that passing the T-31 seconds mark and the start of redundant set sequencing tended to draw a smattering of applause. The cold hard truth was that it meant nothing more than the detection of problems had been turned over to the computer and thus, anything that would keep you from flying could now be detected several million times faster than when you are off of the sequencer. So there was really nothing to cheer about.

In the final seconds prior to the launch I went and stood on the bleachers with the real VIPs. The guy standing next to me was armed with a Super 8 movie camera. At main engine start he raised the camera to his eye, pulled the trigger and began filming. I guess he didn't expect what those of us who had been there for the STS-1 launch had already experienced. A few moments after SRB ignition the Shuttle reached out and grabbed us compelling everyone to scream "GO BABY, GO!"

A moment later I glanced over to see the Super 8 movie guy- mesmerized and standing there looking up at the departing Shuttle, his mouth hanging open and his hand with the running movie camera down at his side filming the bleachers. I nudged him with an elbow and got his attention then pointed down at the camera.

"OH!" He said as he returned to filming the launch.

For some reason the Shuttle did that kind of stuff to you.

Being twice as close to the pad as we were during the launch of STS-1, the sound of the launch reached us much more quickly than it had the first time. Additionally, there was a loud crackle that we had not heard during STS-1. One of the Saturn V veterans standing nearby told me afterward that the sound of this launch was a bit closer to a Saturn.

Again the applause broke out among the crowd as the SRBs separated and dropped away and we all began listening intently to the assorted audio sources giving launch information. At main engine cut-off, there was a distinct cheer from several folks who, no doubt, knew the significance of the MECO call.

A little more than 8 minutes after liftoff the United States had accomplished something never before done; we had reused a spaceflight vehicle for two manned flights. Although an unmanned Gemini II capsule had been reused in an unmanned MOL test flight, this time there was a lot more at risk; Engle and Truly.

There was not the mass sort-of-carnival atmosphere that there had been on the riverbank during STS-1. Of course there were not a half million insane space watchers lined up elbow to elbow as far as the eye could see at the VIP site either. The folks at the VIP site were just as happy, but in lesser numbers. That nice lady with the postal covers wished me good luck in working my way through school and her charming words were caught on my tape recording of the launch. COLUMBIA was safely in orbit and soon we were safely back aboard the bus- feeling that strange sense of pride, as if we had launched COLUMBIA ourselves.

More than three decades after the launch of STS-2, I still have that "collector's item" postal cover that I sent to my folks. I figure it's worth about $1.75. On the 30th anniversary of the STS-2 launch I took it out, sat it on my desk and remembered the launch and the kindness of that nice lady who took pity on an impoverished college kid that morning. I even bought some cheap strawberry preserves, just so I could make a well-squished peanut butter sandwich. It strikes me that at every Space Shuttle launch, in fact every manned spaceflight launch, pleasant people just like that lady gather in a completely joyful atmosphere. You can ask yourself how often is it that anywhere in America crowds of people, upward of a million at a time, from all different backgrounds, gather in one place and are all happy, proud, pleasant and friendly. Without any taking of sides, protesting, shouting, political smears, hatred, vilification, damage and violence, they come only to witness and celebrate the peaceful advancement of human civilization. This perhaps is the most overlooked benefit of United States human spaceflight. (See Image 9, page 76.)

STS-2:
EDDY TOWER, IT'S COLUMBIA

Once COLUMBIA was in orbit there was only one way for us space-buffs to keep track of the mission and that was by way of the TV news networks. CNN, being new and desperate for content, was doing their best to give continuous coverage. Most of us slept on the bus ride back to Daytona and since I had the day off, once I got to my own bed I managed to sleep as if I had been hit in the head with a hockey stick... again. I woke up just in time catch the evening news; the news was not good. NBC's John Chancellor announced that the Shuttle had a problem that was going to bring it back 70 hours sooner than planned. The number 1 fuel cell failed shortly after the COLUMBIA got into orbit and Mission Control had decided to make this "an abbreviated mission." NBC's report of a 70 hour deduction in the mission time line, however, was a bit inflated. The mission was actually cut by just over two days rather than three days.

In spite of the time-line abbreviation, Engle and Truly had a mission to accomplish and went to work trying to cram in as many Designated Test Objectives (DTO) as they could. One of their primary DTOs was to put the Remote Manipulator System (RMS) arm through its paces. Fondly called "the Canada arm," this first workout did not include its lifting anything, but rather was a systematic exercising of the arm as dictated by preflight planning. The arm checked out just fine and thus allowed the crew to check off one of the most important DTOs of the mission.

Astronauts have always said that flying in space does not require as much sleep as working on Earth. Thus, the crew of STS-2 were able to skip a great deal of their scheduled sleep time and apply those precious hours toward accomplishing mission objectives before the early termination of the flight. Officially, NASA would later state that in spite of the abbreviated mission, Engle and Truly had completed 90% of their objectives. Now, there was just one little detail left: the landing.

Reentry and landing of the COLUMBIA on STS-2 would be the first time that a reusable manned spacecraft had ever returned from orbit a second time. At the time, there was one other manned vehicle that had reached space and then returned to be reused multiple times. That vehicle was the X-15. More through happenstance than through planning, Joe Engle, the one man in the active ranks of astronauts who had flown the X-15, was now at the controls of the Space Shuttle COLUMBIA. His task during the return of STS-2 was one that fit his stick-n-rudder test pilot breeding just fine. Engle was to be the first and only pilot to manually fly a winged vehicle all the way down from orbit and Mach 24 to wheels stop on the runway. The only break in that exercise would be during the landing pattern, when he would hand over the controls to Dick Truly and allow him to fly the turn from "the 180 to the 90" degree points, or in pilot talk, "the downwind to base." Considering that Engle had more hypersonic stick time in his logbook than any other NASA astronaut, this final DTO was in the right hands indeed.

With more than two dozen specific maneuvers to be

flown beginning at Mach 24, the crew tried to put aside being tired and dehydrated and worked at their procedures in preparation for reentry. NASA was keen to see what types of hand control authority and stability the orbiter had at high Mach numbers and the only way to get that data was to hand-fly the vehicle. Engle increased the angle of attack and decreased it in small increments of about five degrees. He also "kicked the rudder" and swept the bank angle. Each time the performance data was recorded for later analysis. Although much had been previously gleaned from wind tunnel exercises, such information still has a lot of variables that can only be narrowed by way of actual flight. As it turned out, a great deal of useful data was collected through Engle's hand-flying and subsequently changes were made in the programming of the automatic flight control system of the Shuttle.

Fortunately, after having his eyes accidentally dilated before reentry by scopolamine contaminating his fingers, Truly was able to squint out enough reading of the cue cards to get by, and Engle had memorized all of the maneuvers anyway, so the reentry went along somewhat normally.

The winds at Edwards were strong aloft, upward of 90 knots at 30,000 feet, and at ground level they were strengthening into the 20s. For that reason the orbiter's runway was changed shortly before reentry. Originally STS-2 was supposed to conduct a crosswind landing, but that test was deleted as the surface winds strengthened beyond the orbiter's predicted crosswind component. Being a pilot, I sat in front of my TV set and mentally compensated for the winds aloft in spite of the fact that I was more than 2,000 miles away from Edwards Air Force Base and had nothing to do with the Shuttle other than watching it on TV.

Joe Engle found that once he was over top of Edwards

his long time experience at that airfield suddenly brought back a confidence that he was just bringing another airplane home to land on the dry lake. It was a comfort and familiarity that allows a pilot to easily click into "the zone." On energy and on course, Engle guided COLUMBIA to a perfect landing. Beside him was his crewmate, teammate and his Shuttle PLT since the mid 1970s, Dick Truly; a better combination could never have been found.

Many months prior to the flight, Engle had visited the control tower at Edwards and while joking with one of the controllers he quipped that he would give him a call on final approach. The controller replied "I'll clear ya." Although communications were supposed to be strictly with Houston, as Engle rolled COLUMBIA onto final approach he called the tower and said,

"Eddy Tower, it's COLUMBIA rolling out on high final. I'll call the gear on the flare."

To which the controller dutifully responded,

"Roger, COLUMBIA, you're cleared number one. Call your gear."

That exchange left many in Houston scratching their heads and wondering who was extraneously talking on the frequency, the folks at Edwards, however, loved it.

Some 200,000 visitors had gathered at the field to watch COLUMBIA return. In a fitting tribute to the importance of the mission, CBS News' long-time spaceflight anchorman Walter Cronkite had come out of retirement to host the network's broadcast of the landing from Edwards. Millions of television viewers watched as Engle and Truly made their third Shuttle landing; two having been done with the ENTERPRISE and now one with COLUMBIA.

I finished my tape recording of the mission and marked STS-2 as the second of only two bright spots for me in the year 1981, with the first being STS-1. Of course I had high hopes that 1982 would be better; perhaps there would be more Shuttle missions launched and I would have additional escapes from Kmart. Surely, with flight rates scheduled to dramatically increase, my job at Kmart had to get better; that is, unless they transferred me to the stinkin' Garden Shop.

STS-3:
ON LAUNCH DAY, "THEY" DON'T EXIST

In looking back over the decades to the flight of STS-3 there is one thing to keep clearly in context: this was a TEST flight. Although the Shuttle had flown two previous times, STS-3 was the next in the series of four flight tests intended to seek out and reveal flaws in the whole system. Some people, especially some in today's Internet, arm-chair, know-it-all breed of self-proclaimed spaceflight "experts" seem to forget or simply ignore the fact that there were four Shuttle flights that were of a test nature. Out of that confused fog of un-researched and ill-informed opinions there sprouts the myth of the STS-3 "Wheelie Landing," which we will debunk in the end of this chapter.

As the year 1982 started out, my job at the Daytona Kmart, which I thought could not get any worse, got worse. I found myself transferred out to the "Garden Shop," which is similar to being sent from working in the prison library to working in swamp reclamation. I think it had something to with my manager in the cosmetics and pharmacy department nagging me to do "PAs," or the short, spoken, in-store commercials that each employee was expected to do on the store intercom. They pestered us to do these all the time, because they were supposed to be free advertising. Frankly, I found them to be just a pain in the ass, and almost as annoying as the managers who pestered me to do one.

Finally, I asked,

"What should I PA?"

And my Cosmetics and Pharmacy department manager simply barked,

"Just take any item off the shelf, just pick one!"

"Okay," I asked, "what should I say about it?"

"Just read what it says on the package," he snarled while walking away.

There followed "The great PA'ing of glycerin suppositories incident." I just grabbed a box of them off the shelf, went to the PA and began reading what it said on the label using my best TV game show announcer voice. You know, the stuff about how effective it was and how easy they were to insert and where to insert them. I will never forget the look on that assistant manager's face as he came dashing toward me from the back of the store. Next thing I knew, I was working in the Garden Shop. But, they never bugged me to PA stuff anymore. Perhaps that was because we had 40 pound bags of cow manure in stock there.

In spite of all of that, the outlook for spaceflight was pretty good for 1982. A new orbiter, the CHALLENGER was to be delivered to KSC in the summer, plus four and perhaps even five missions were slated to fly during the year. If that happened, it would be the first time since 1973 that three manned launches had flown from US soil in a single calendar year. As someone who had grown up with spaceflight, that resonated with me.

Personally, I had the great fortune to witness the first two Shuttle launches from two different perspectives: STS-1 from the banks of the Indian River and STS-2 from the VIP site. For the launch of STS-3, I was lucky enough to have my parents and younger brother visiting Florida during the event. Venturing down from Michigan in my Dad's second-hand motor home, they were seeking to relieve me of my normal working-your-way-through-college diet of Rice-a-roni and peanut butter for at least a week. As a bonus, they had scheduled their visit during the launch of COLUMBIA and we were going to head down and see it as soon as I got off of work.

Freed from my service in the living hell that was the Daytona Kmart's garden shop at 4:00 pm sharp on March 21, 1982, I left the loading of pine bark nuggets and cow manure to someone else and boarded the family motor home. We set out for the Space Coast. The folks wanted to take the scenic route down US1, and so southbound we rattled toward Titusville.

Along the way my Dad turned to me and asked, "So, where are ya' gonna have us park this beast?"

"I'll let ya' know when I see it," I simply shrugged and replied.

What I knew, but my Dad was not aware of, was that on a launch day, almost any place within 25 miles of the Kennedy Space Center becomes a public campground.

Just after US1 turned into the town of Titusville, a vacant piece of open ground caught my eye near the river south of the intersection of the highway and Max Brewer Parkway.

"Right there!" I exclaimed, pointing at the open lot. "Just pull in right there!"

Dad reluctantly pulled the land boat onto the open dirt lot. As we came to a stop it was clear that there were already several campers staked out there. Stepping out of the motor home I did my best Jake Blues arriving at the "Country Bunker" impression.

"Yep, this is the place."

Dad was not at all convinced.

"What if they come and run us otta here?" he asked doubtfully.

"Don't worry," I assured him, "on the night before a launch 'they' don't exist."

Dad worried most of the evening. People from the Midwest are very uncomfortable about invading other folk's property without an invitation or a paid camping spot. But as the evening wore on and the once open lot became packed with campers, my Dad turned off his mid-Michigan worry switch and started to relax like the rest of us.

(See Image 10, page 77.) Our little camping spot was exactly 12.2 miles due west of Launch Complex 39A. As the sun set, the spot lights on the pad turned the waiting Space Shuttle rightfully into the center of attention. My Mom was absolutely transfixed by the Shuttle illuminated at the pad and simply could not take her attention away from it. She was not alone, as most of the campers there also were first-timers to a space launch. On the other hand, I was kept busy monitoring news reports on launch status as best I could, mainly by way of local AM radio. Unlike STS-1, this time there were plenty of TVs and radios to be found in the area. Much like STS-1, however, very few in the crowd understood the details of the countdown and the massive amount of glitches that could trigger a scrub. For the first time it dawned on me that I sort of wished I was one of those people who did not know how many things could go wrong and delay the launch. It was a feeling I would re-live three decades and 122 Shuttles later during STS-125.

Of course Mom took the liberty of telling nearby campers that her son, ya' know, the guy in the aviator sunglasses standing down there by the river talking to a crowd about the spaceflight, knew all about the Shuttle- because he was a pilot studying Aeronautical Science. Of course that little boast got out among the retired folks camped nearby and morphed into, "That guy is an astronaut." Try convincing a crowd of old folks that you are NOT an astronaut. Explaining that you are working your way through college, you only have 200 flight hours in little Cessnas. That you don't work for NASA, you work for Kmart. It should be easy, but it ain't; one old lady wanted me to pet her dog, then she said now she could tell the people back home that fluffy was petted by an astronaut! Finally I decided it would be best if I just spent the evening in the motor home and let the rumor mill die out. Mom just said she didn't know where they got that idea. Ugh.

STS-3:
MAN! LOOK AT HER GO!

Following 70 days in the Orbiter Processing Facility after STS-2, COLUMBIA had been mated to the External Tank (ET) in the VAB on February 3, 1982, and rolled out to Pad 39A just 13 days later. STS-3 was the first Shuttle stack to have the now well-known "orange" ET. Even after the ETs were in production, NASA was engaged in the process of weight scrubbing. After some extensive testing, it was decided that the ET's spray-on CPR-488 foam insulation was strong enough to tolerate the heating of the high-speed airflow during the ascent. For that reason the white-colored Fire Retardant Latex (FRL) that was used as an overcoat on the tank was deleted on later tanks following STS-2, the first of which flew on STS-3. Deletion of the FRL not only saved a small amount of money and man-hours in production, but also saved 595 pounds of weight. Oddly, when a new ET was rolled out of assembly with its fresh CPR-488 coat on, it was not orange, but rather was a greenish yellow color. Solar ultra violet rays caused the foam to turn orange over time and as it was exposed to more and more sunlight it turned an orangish brown in color – a Space Shuttle sun tan. Doing some launch day announcing for ABC News, astronaut Gene Cernan speculated that they may later mix a white pigment with the CPR-488 to make the tank white again. Of course that never happened, but that thought illustrates just how odd that orange tank appeared when stacked as a spaceflight booster in the 1982 era.

Sporting its orange ET, the countdown for STS-3 was normal up until very late on the night before the launch. A malfunction on a nitrogen gas line in some ground support equipment delayed fueling operations for a short time and it looked like a bad glitch to those of us on the outside. Just before dawn, however, NASA PAO announced that the delay would be just one hour in length. Oddly, at our little campsite, rumors spread saying everything from "Pack it up and go home" to "Problem? There's no problem." At the time, I found it was best to just stay glued to the AM radio and avoid the other campers.

Following a one-hour delay, COLUMBIA's crew, Commander (CDR) Jack Lousma and Pilot (PLT) Gordon Fullerton went aboard and were strapped in. Originally, Lousma had been selected as the PLT for STS-3 and went into training with Fred Haise who had been CDR of the Shuttle ENTERPRISE while conducting the Approach and Landing Tests back in 1977. Their STS-3 mission was scheduled to be the rescue of Skylab, which was why Lousma, a former Skylab astronaut, was selected for it. However, the best laid plans of NASA soon began to fall apart as the Shuttle's development began to experience delays and the sun's activity began to grow. The development schedule pushed STS-3 back by nearly two years and the increased solar activity caused the Earth's atmosphere to swell. The result was that the atmospheric influence on Skylab caused its orbit to decay at a far greater rate than expected. Skylab was going to reenter sooner than planned. For that reason the STS-3 crew of Haise and Lousma was moved up to STS-2. The schedule of Shuttle development, however, soon pushed completely beyond the date of Skylab's reentry. The crew was returned to STS-3 and the Skylab rescue mission was canceled. Eventually opportunities motivated Fred Haise to retire from NASA and Jack Lousma was moved into the CDR seat of STS-3 and given Gordon Fullerton as his PLT. Fullerton had actually been Fred Haise's PLT in the Approach and Landing Test missions aboard the ENTERPRISE and he also had composed many of the checklists and procedures now being used on the Shuttle. Now he would take that experience and make his first trip into space.

At 11:00:00 a.m. Eastern Time, the bolts blew, the SRBs ignited and the STS-3 stack lifted off. The burst of sun-bright flame and billows of smoke and steam at Pad 39A set off cheers and screams from every direction around KSC. About 17 seconds later, as the first-timers in our little campsite started to realize that they could not hear the Shuttle, it was then that COLUMBIA reached out for the third time, took hold of every soul and shook us to the point where we knew the true meaning of glory. Thrilled screams and cheers now reflexively burst from the crowd at a higher pitch. For a moment I could feel the ground actually shake. Looking down I saw a puddle nearby and its water was vibrating. I tapped my Mom on the shoulder and pointed down at the reverberating water. She glanced down, squealed with delight and went back to watching COLUMBIA climb. Dad was spell-bound and just kept saying,

"Man! Look at her go!"

There were broken cloud decks in the launch area, but from our location the launch was mostly un-obscured. Raining fire from her SRBs COLUMBIA climbed with the determination of a homesick angle. This time, instead of my family watching me entranced by a space launch, I got the joy of standing back and watching all of them capti-vated by the wonder of America's space program.

Following SRB separation the COLUMBIA once again became a bright star rapidly fading into the morning sky. In a phenomena that would accompany every Shuttle launch for the next three decades, the crowd of spectators broke into spontaneous applause that no one directly involved with the mission could hear. Straining their eyes toward the sky, many tried to watch the Shuttle's departure for as long as humanly possible before turning away and heading home. I was guilty of that myself. Then I looked at my Dad and Mom and little brother.

"THAT," I exclaimed proudly, "is what it's all about."

Mom wiped tears from her eyes, Dad gave that relieved laugh that he always used when he had no words for a given event and my younger brother simply kept saying words such as "Wow" and "Cool." It was an experience that they would take home and share with their friends and relatives for decades to come.

Of course STS-3 still had a long way to go before in-sertion into orbit. On the way uphill the Number 3 Aux-iliary Power Unit began to show a rising temperature and Mission Control ordered the crew to "secure" it. Although this glitch caught the attention of the news media, it made little difference in the progress of the mission. By the time that the launch spectators finally got their collective breath, Main Engine Cutoff had occurred. Shortly thereafter a series of Orbital Maneuvering System engine burns took place and COLUMBIA was in orbit for the third time.

Joining the traffic jam headed away from KSC, I found myself riding among a herd of dazzled Americans who were now fully aware of what their tax dollars budgeted to NASA could do. NASA announced that once again an estimated one million people had flooded into the area around KSC to watch the launch. Prior to launch, President Reagan had dedicated the flight to the people of Afghanistan who were embroiled in conflict with our Cold War enemies, the Soviet Russians. Looking back across the years, it is interesting to see how things have changed.

STS-3:
DTOS AND THE MYTH OF
THE "WHEELIE LANDING"

Officially NASA's objectives for the STS-3 mission were to "Demonstrate ascent, on orbit, and entry performance under conditions more demanding than STS-2 conditions. Extend orbital flight duration. Conduct long duration thermal soak tests. To conduct scientific and applications research with an attached payload." The crew went directly into the thermal test profile, the first part of which was establishing a baseline by placing COLUMBIA into a slow roll, something that astronauts like to call "rotisserie mode." This "passive thermal control" mode was done for three 10-hour periods. In addition to that, the orbiter was placed into a "tail to the sun" attitude, which was maintained for a period of 30 hours. Then the orbiter also was placed with its payload bay pointing toward the sun for 26 hours. Finally, COLUMBIA was placed in an attitude with her nose to the sun for an 80-hour period of time. Data from each of these attitudes was collected and transmitted down to Mission Control.

Experiments ranging from "electrophoresis equipment verification testing" and "dynamic acoustic and thermal environment experiments" to an "insect in-flight motion study" were being conducted by the crew as COLUMBIA basked in the sun. The news media gave the most attention to the insects in flight study because it was easy to understand, especially for most TV news producers. It was developed by a high school senior, Todd Nelson. When you saw him interviewed, you got the distinct impression that he was far more intelligent than the people interviewing him. Although the news people may have thought that Todd's experiment was something simple enough that they may be able to fully understand it, Todd either proved them wrong or at least made them work for it.

Of all the networks, CNN provided the best coverage of STS-3. That was, of course, because the toddling two-year-old network needed content. So, every time the Shuttle down-linked pictures, CNN was there, much to every space-buff's delight.

Many of the experiments carried aboard STS-3 were listed as Detailed Test Objectives, or DTOs. For the full schedule duration of the mission the two-man crew worked at systematically completing their DTOs. Finally, on the mission's last scheduled day the two astronauts suited up, closed the payload bay doors and prepared for reentry. The final set of DTOs would involve the reentry and landing.

Heavy rains in California had wetted the normally dry lakebed at Edwards Air Force Base until the surface was "the consistency of Cream of Wheat." The flight test nature of the STS-3 mission dictated that the landing was to be conducted on a dry lake if at all possible. At this point in the Shuttle program the runway at KSC was untried. In fact, only one Shuttle orbiter, the ENTERPRISE, had made a landing on a concrete runway and that was a single landing made at Edwards back in 1977 during the ALT. NASA was simply not ready to allow the Shuttle to land on the confines of the concrete runway yet. Oddly, that lone runway landing had been made by a two-man crew, the

PLT of which had been Gordon Fullerton. That fact aside, NASA had elected, two weeks prior to the STS-3 launch, to land on the dry lake at White Sands, New Mexico. Unfortunately, on the scheduled landing day, an occasional, but classic sandstorm suddenly blew up and brought with it severe turbulence, low visibility and drifts of gypsum powder across the runway. STS-3's landing was waved off for 24 hours.

Dawn the following day at White Sands revealed absolutely perfect weather for the landing. This segment of the mission was scheduled to be test piloting to the greatest degree as the final DTOs would be accomplished. Jack Lousma was required to test the auto-land system to a point far beyond normal operation and far beyond any previous flight. He was to take over manually at scheduled points during the entry and put in some small control inputs such as forward stick to neutral stick to back stick than to neutral again, all at one second intervals. Then he was to reach up on the glare shield and punch the button that would activate the auto-land. In each of these cases the crew was to note how the auto-land responded. Lousma estimated that he did this procedure about 10 times. Interlaced with that series of tests, a similar test sequence was performed in the roll axis as well as with the body flap. The same exercise had been performed in the simulator numerous times, but what the crew of STS-3 was to discover was that the simulator and the actual orbiter did not perform alike at some points.

In addition to the auto-land response DTO, the crew also was scheduled to test the auto-land all the way down the flight path, nearly to the ground. It is worth making a note at this point in the story that the computer's auto-land software had not yet been written for the final flare, touchdown and rollout. The auto-land software had only been written to the point of intercept of the inner glide slope. For those of you reading who have not flown high performance or heavy aircraft, that sort of an approach may sound like a milk run, but in fact it is not. Most pilots of such aircraft would rather hand-fly it down. Personally, I prefer to hand-fly a turbo prop from about 10,000 feet down and a jet from 18,000 feet down. Every Shuttle pilot I have talked to feels the same way and would rather hand-fly as much as they can all the way down. But in the case of STS-3, Jack Lousma's DTO was to ring out the auto-land, and so he did.

CDR Lousma executed the testing through reentry and the switchovers appeared to be normal. Then, as directed by the mission profile, he engaged the auto-land at 12,000 feet on the outer glide slope. At that time the Shuttle approach PAPI, a series of lights located beside the runway that gives the pilot visual information concerning his glide slope, indicated two red and two white on a 19-degree glide slope and on center line.

"That was the last time I saw a stabilized airspeed," Lousma recalled, "although the automatic system controlled OGS (Outer Glide Slope) well, including the transition from OGS to IGS (Inner Glide Slope)."

Unexpectedly the auto-land system made a slight right roll correction, probably to nullify the effect of a right crosswind at that altitude. Then the crew felt the speed brakes close immediately. This was abnormal and allowed the orbiter to accelerate to 285 knots. These "speed brakes" consisted of the rudder splitting in half vertically and hydraulically extending out into the airflow symmetrically to each side and thus providing a high degree of drag. Normally in a hand-flown approach the Shuttle pilots use the speed

ALT astronauts Fred Haise (L) and Gordon Fullerton (R).

Image 1

ENTERPRISE separates from the Shuttle Carrier aircraft, NASA 905 on August 12, 1977 to make its first free flight.

Image 2

Ed Hengeveld photo showing the ventral fins used on the STA to simulated the orbiter's sideways "lurch." Photo used with permission.

Image 3

**Shuttle orbiter COLUMBIA on its way to KSC,
March, 1979; minus a lot of tiles.**

Image 4

Image 5

Launch day for STS-1 and Jules Bergman kept saying they were
going to scrub. We wanted to strangle him, but he was right.

Image 6

**STS-1 bathed in the spotlights.
We couldn't take our eyes off of it.**

As STS-1 thundered into the sky we cheered
shouted and screamed like idiots. Then it
reached out and shook us with its glory.

Image 7

When COLUMBIA's wheels stopped America was taken
out of the "era of limits" and into the era of the Shuttle.

Image 8

Postal cover given to me by a kind lady at STS-2
along with orders to send it to my folks back home
because one day it'll be a collector's item.

Image 9

Image 10

My Dad and I at STS-3
with the family's second-hand motor home.

Image 11

Author with Jack Lousma
aboard cruise ship c. COLUMBUS.

Image 12

Author's scratch-built orbiter.
A delight for my drunken roommates.

Awaiting the landing of STS-4,
the orbiter CHALLENGER, both
STAs and President Reagan.

Image 13

TV, live from STS-5.

Image 14

STS-6 and the first US spacewalk
since Skylab nearly a decade earlier.

Image 15

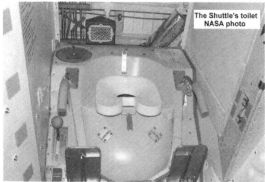

The Shuttle's toilet
NASA photo

Image 16

The news media's darling during STS-7 was
Sally Ride, but they fixated on the unisex toilet too.

NASA photo

Image 17

Bruce McCandless conducted the world's
first un-tethered EVA using the manned
maneuvering unit- his specialty at NASA.

Image 18

My press I.D. for the 22nd
Shuttle launch, STS-61-A.

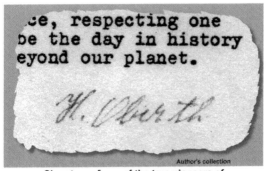

...ce, respecting one
be the day in history
eyond our planet.

H. Oberth

Author's collection

Signature of one of the true pioneers of
spaceflight; Professor Hermann Oberth.

Image 19

Standing just a few yards away from me,
Christa McAuliffe is thrilled by the 61A launch.

NASA photo

Image 20

Image 21

This is me bringing in the T-303 Crusader, single-engine, back-course approach, runway 25R, Daytona Beach Regional Airport.

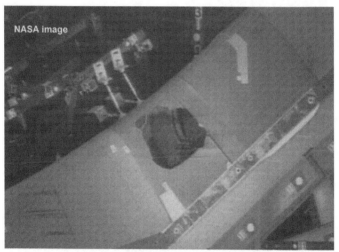

Engineers at the Southwest Research Institute used a section of the leading edge from the shuttle ENTERPRISE to test the effects of a frozen chunk of foam impacting the reinforced carbon-carbon surface. The result was a huge hole.

Image 22

**STS-110, amazingly it was my
Florida girl's first in-person
Shuttle launch.**

Image 23

**The button that told everyone that I was
a VIP and not a slob... today anyway.**

Image 24

Image 25

STS-131's EVA at the ISS and
the view from my hospital bed.

Image 26

Elbow to elbow the KSC press site is packed for STS-135.

Image 27

The broadcast buildings from which the "big 3" networks once
brought Apollo, Skylab and the Shuttle into the world's living rooms.

brakes in degrees to manage the orbiter's energy and blend airspeed and altitude. As the auto-land computer sensed the speed increase, it opened the speed brakes again to a greater than normal degree. Now the airspeed slowed to a speed which was below a software set-switch that would automatically fully close the speed brakes at 4,000 feet if the speed was too low. The speed brakes were not designed to move suddenly from highly open to fully closed and then back again, but that was what the auto-land was commanding. In this critical portion of the approach the auto-land was over-correcting the travel of the speed brakes. On a manual approach the crew would have closed the speed brakes at 2,500 feet to prevent them from cross-coupling with the pre-flare pull-up at 1,750 feet. On the STS-3 auto-land approach the computer commanded the speed brakes closed 1,500 feet early, which caused an acceleration prior to entering the pre-flare that was carried to the end of the pre-flare.

In short, the auto-land system was causing wide swings of the speed brakes during the most critical portion of the landing, rather than mimicking the inputs of a manual approach. It was later discovered that the software in the simulator that everyone had considered to be the mirror image of the software in the orbiter was not that at all.

As directed in the flight plan, Lousma took over manual control when the orbiter was stabilized on IGS. This took place between 200 and 150 feet AGL. As he took control he noted that the controls "felt different" than they should at that point. The vehicle was carrying more airspeed than normal at that phase of flight. Although he was 5 knots over the gear deploy speed he called for the gear and Fullerton lowered the landing gear. It is important to note here, again for any non-pilots who may be reading this, that deployment of landing gear is normally dependent on speed and not the observations of persons on the ground or the proximity of the aircraft to that ground. In the case of STS-3, to people on the ground it appeared as if the gear had come down low and late. In fact it was deployed somewhat early as the vehicle was 5 knots too fast.

Another result of the higher speed was that the touch-down point was now farther down the runway than desired. Like any good test pilot, Lousma negated the error by simply planting the aircraft on the runway. It is important here to also note one thing about the Shuttle that a lot of people do not understand. When rolling with all of their wheels on the ground the Shuttle orbiters had a negative Angle Of Attack (AOA). Thus during the landing rollout after the main gear was on the ground and the vehicle began to slow the nose would drop through from a positive AOA, to a neutral and then to a negative AOA very rapidly. The pilot was required to compensate by consciously "flying" the nose down to the ground. Originally the orbiter's nose gear had been designed with a longer strut to compensate for this characteristic, but a subsequent weight scrub had negated that idea. Lousma was well-prepared for this characteristic, but as COLUMBIA's main gear contacted the runway the nose immediately began to go down. The plan, however, had been for the CDR to hold nose up and perform aerodynamic braking from the point of touch-down until slowing to 165 knots. Instead, the COLUMBIA's nose gear was now headed toward the runway at 220 knots. Instinctively, Lousma made a quick pitch-up input with the rotational hand controller, but the nose continued down. He immediately entered a second input which was greeted with a rapid nose up response. He corrected by putting an additional nose down response and this time regained authority and the nose wheels were placed on the runway. The orbiter rolled to a stop 13,723 feet down the runway.

It was later discovered that there was a divergence in the longitudinal contrast software for the Shuttle's landing configuration. That, combined with the additional speed that the auto-land system had left the orbiter with, conflicted with the gain setting in the software. This caused the fly-by-wire system to impose an abnormal delay between the pilot's inputs into the hand controller and the movement of the control surfaces. In simpler terms, (engineers please forgive me for this simplification) the first stick input to counter the dropping of the nose was delayed because the software sensed that the orbiter was going too fast for such a command to be executed. Then when the second input was made the software added it to the first command and then that total was transmitted to the control surface which responded by commanding the total movement to the aerodynamic control surfaces. Lousma had nothing to do with this process other than making intuitive corrections. Had he done nothing, the nose gear would have hit the runway at 220 knots and may very well have been damaged or sheared off.

Of course to the uninformed observer, such as most reporters in the TV news media and some present-day Internet "experts," it appeared as if Lousma had botched the landing. In one good example of this misconception CBS news' reporter Terry Drinkwater hyperbolized on the evening news that day by reporting that this was;

"The Shuttle's least perfect landing." He then went on to further to mindlessly exaggerate; "The landing gear is programmed to come down when the spacecraft slows to 311 miles per hour, (270 knots,) but when the speed finally dropped to that, the COLUMBIA was extremely low. There were only 5 seconds between wheels down and touchdown. Close! Next, as the nose seemed to be gently settling, suddenly it lifted again. Then apparent control, but the force of the forward speed and the weight on the nose gear was close to its tolerance." He added that this was likely caused by of a gust of wind or more likely a computer error, or pilot mistake.'"

Frankly, the only parts of that statement that were correct was the gear speed and the term "computer error".

Thus began the myth of the "wheelie landing."

Some people then and now picture Jack Lousma in a state of embarrassment immediately after the landing of STS-3. In fact, quite the opposite is true. He was happy and excited and somewhat tickled that on this test flight, during the entry, approach and landing, the crew had uncovered a series of flaws in the auto-land system as well as the impact of those flaws on the software for the fly-by-wire system. Those problems could now be corrected so that future Shuttle pilots would not experience the same problems. That was the purpose of his flight: to test. It is also worth denoting the fact that on the previous two flights, as well as all of the ALT flights, the crews had only tested the auto-land for very brief periods of flight, and no one prior to STS-3 had tested it all the way down to the IGS, let alone exercised it as had been done by the STS-3 crew. This was flight test at its best and the results improved future missions.

Yet, even as of this writing, more than three decades after STS-3, you can look on YouTube and find videos of the "wheelie landing." And if you have a strong stomach, you can read the moronic comments about it left by people whose total flight experience extends no farther than their computer's keyboard, and whose research into the event goes no farther than repeating the quips that others have posted. The same is sadly true of most Internet spaceflight forums and their self-certified Shuttle "experts."

Jack Lousma retired from NASA in 1983 and went to serve as the President of CAMUS Inc. Gordon Fullerton went on to the CDR's seat on the 19th Shuttle mission, STS-51F. Interestingly, unlike many other astronauts, Fullerton's pilot roots were not in fighter planes- rather he was a bomber pilot who started out in the B-47 with the Strategic Air Command. He flew the retirement flight of the famed 008 B-52 "Balls 8" mother ship; an honor in any bomber pilot's logbook. Fullerton passed away on August 21, 2013, from complications due to a stroke he suffered in 2009.

As a post script to this chapter, in the autumn of 2001, I had been hired to be an "enhancement speaker and guide" on the Great Lakes aboard the cruise ship C. COLUMBUS. When I was hired they informed me that the other speaker would be Astronaut Jack Lousma. At the time they asked if I knew who he was. I played it cool, "Oh, yeah, I know who he is." Of course I could hardly wait to get aboard the boat. Unfortunately, my duties aboard the vessel left very little time to just hang out with Mr. Lousma. We did get a couple of chances to just stand and talk, however. On the other hand, my Mom, who I had taken along as my guest since my wife refused to go along on "another cruise," became pals with Mrs. Lousma. One day, after Mr. Lousma and I had each finished our individual presentations, we were standing there chatting about the Shuttle and my Mom spoke up;

"Ya' know," she boasted in the best of mid-western manners, "I was down there and saw one of those Shuttles take off."

"Mom…" I placed my hand on her shoulder and broke the news to her, "you saw HIS Shuttle launch."

We all had a good laugh at her expense. (See Image 11, page 77.)

STS-4:
HOW COULD I SAY NO?

It was mid-summer 1982, and with the Fourth of July coming up, someone had given me a large bottle rocket with which to celebrate our nation's birthday. Inspired after attending the STS-4 launch, I decided that a better use for the big bottle rocket was as a little Shuttle booster. I painted it ET orange, made some little mock SRBs to glue on the sides and then, to make it even more fun, I scratch-built a tiny orbiter out of paper and a little bit of balsa wood, to ride on the bottle rocket. I rigged a make-shift hook on the nose of the orbiter that went under the plastic nosecone of the rocket so that at the right moment, when the rocket popped the orbiter could just release and fly. I trimmed the bottle rocket stick to the booster length squared (optimum for stability and altitude on a bottle rocket, by the way) and then had the whole thing sitting on my desk as a display to my own insanity.

(See Image 12, page 77.) On July 4, I watched the STS-4 landing on TV with two of my friends from school—Dan and Joe. It was blistering hot outside, and our typical rented-to-college-guys crummy house in Holly Hill, Florida had no air conditioning. So later on we were sitting around and the other two guys were getting very happy drinking rum and Cokes. Since I am a lifelong non-drinker, I just hung out and enjoyed the fact that I was not hauling around bags of cow manure at the Kmart Garden Shop today. As the day went on the guys got more and more "happy" and started bugging me about my fireworks Shuttle. I demonstrated in a toss how well the orbiter flew, and that resulted in additional pestering about launching it. After an afternoon of drunken dares, pestering and nagging they shifted to saying that launching it would be a great way to "celebrate" STS-4.

How could I say no?

By now these two guys were too inebriated to drive to any launching site and so it was decided to just launch from the front yard. Our house, on Daytona Avenue, was heavily covered by very large trees, so I got one of the dozen or so Coke bottles that the drunks had emptied, put my bottle-rocket Shuttle stack on it, aimed for biggest hole in the tree canopy and lit the fuse.

Unexpectedly, the bottle rocket shot up through a different hole in the trees and went completely out of sight. We heard the fireworks "pop!" that everyone was sure had signaled the end of my mini STS-4. The guys howled with laughter, but that little orbiter, as it would turn out, had other ideas.

STS-4:
KSC SECURITY DOES NOT
HAVE A SENSE OF HUMOR.

Just a week earlier, on the 27th day of June, 1982, the Space Shuttle program was slightly more than 14 months old. This was launch day for STS-4 and those of us who were there to see it were sure that we were witnessing another flight of what NASA called "the primary space vehicle for the foreseeable future." None of us who grew up with spaceflight dreamed that "the foreseeable future" would come and go in just three short decades.

This fourth launch of the Space Shuttle was scheduled to be the last of the flight test series for the Space Transportation System. After the seven-day mission the Space Shuttle was to be declared "operational." Of course, that declaration depended largely on the success of this mission that had been officially dubbed simply "STS-4." In the news media, however, the TV networks of the time, after three previous missions, finally decided what they would call the mission. Apparently they thought that the STS-4 moniker was too obscure and NASA-like for general public consumption, so they decided to call it "Space Shuttle 4."

In order to attend the STS-4 launch I had once again teamed up with the same guys from Embry-Riddle who were with me for the first Shuttle launch, my buddies Brian and Jennings. This time, however, instead of camping out all night on the riverbank in Titusville, we were a bit more experienced at Shuttle launch watching. Jennings had scored a causeway pass for his car and we all drove down early in the morning prior to launch. Along the way we discussed some of the unique aspects of the STS-4 mission. One of the primary aspects that captured our attention was the fact that STS-4 was going to be the first Shuttle mission to carry a Department of Defense (DOD) payload. Now anyone reading this who, perhaps was not around in that era should keep in mind that those days were the beginning of the Reagan administration, and the Cold War with the Soviet Union was rapidly growing much, much colder. Thus, the concept of using the Space Shuttle to carry DOD payloads was one of major importance. Driving down toward the Kennedy Space Center we talked and joked about the prospect of carrying DOD cargos on the Shuttle. I'm not sure which one of us came up with the idea, but somewhere along the drive we three college students conceived that it may be fun to arrive at the KSC security gate speaking in thick Russian accents.

"Dah, we are joost happy Amridcan spaceuh boofs, here to zee shootle." "Camra? Ez only short randge feelm." "How 'bout dem Braves?"

An important lesson for everyone reading this: KSC security does NOT have a sense of humor. In fact it is said that they have all had it surgically removed.

Eventually we got through security, onto the causeway at KSC, and found a place to park among thousands of other vehicles. Viewing a Shuttle launch from the causeway in 1982 was very similar to what it would be like throughout the entire Shuttle program. Cars were parked 6 to 14 deep along the roadside, porta-potties were in place, and along the entire length of causeway itself small loud speakers were wired up on stands from which the "loop" of launch control conversation could be heard. On the occasion of STS-4, the only thing that interrupted the neat rows of parked cars was an eight-foot long alligator. Sometime prior to our arrival the alligator had crawled out of the water looking for a warm meal. Having lived in Florida for a few years the three of us knew enough to stay well clear of the beached alligator. Some of the other tourist-types parked among us, however, were not nearly as savvy. I watched in horror as a few individuals allowed their children to crumple up papers and toss them at the alligator. Before long KSC security got wind of the situation, roped off about a 20 foot perimeter around the alligator and posted a guard. It was part of KSC's "Keeping Idiots From Becoming Meals" policy.

Selected as crew for the STS-4 mission were Ken "T.K." Mattingly, commander (CDR) and Henry "Hank" Harts-field, pilot (PLT). Mattingly had flown to the moon 10 years earlier on Apollo 16 as its command module pilot. Hartsfield had formerly been selected for the Air Force's ultra-secret Manned Orbiting Laboratory (MOL) program, but was later transferred to NASA when the MOL was canceled. They would be the last two-man crew to ever fly a Shuttle orbiter.

Assembly of the STS-4 stack began on March 29, 1982, when the aft assemblies of the two SRBs were placed on Mobile Launch Platform (MLP) number 1. That was just seven days after MLP-1 had been used for the launch of STS-3, thus demonstrating NASA's ability to quickly turn around an MLP following a Shuttle launch. The COLUMBIA arrived from White Sands on April 6, and went into the Orbiter Processing Facility (OPF) the following day. A number of fixes were required to be done on COLUMBIA, not the least of which was the removal of the orbiter's malfunctioning toilet and its return to the manufacturer. On April 16, the External Tank was stacked between the two SRBs. The ET itself had been at KSC since January 22, and like its predecessor, as well as all future tanks, it was not painted white. On May 19, COLUMBIA was rolled out of the OPF and over to the VAB. Its stay in the OPF had been just 40 working days; the shortest turn around in the Shuttle program thus far. The orbiter was mated to the stack the following day, May 26, and rolled to Launch Complex 39A. One month later my buddies Brian, Jennings and I were there, minus our fake Russian accents, to watch the final countdown.

One of the unspoken objectives of the STS-4 launch was to actually get the mission launched exactly on schedule. All three of the previous flights had suffered some sort of delay. STS-1 was scrubbed 48 hours for a computer timing error. Then STS-2 was scrubbed for a week due to an APU issue. STS-3 was delayed by one hour due to a problem with ground support equipment. In spite of the fact that these missions were all of a flight test nature, critics of the program made the most of the delays asking if the STS was too complex to become what NASA had promised: a reliable "space truck."

An event that could have caused a delay in the launch took place on the afternoon before launch day when one of those "typical" Florida thunderstorms blew up right over LC39. Lightning, heavy rain and hail events took place all around the pad. Although none of the lightning struck the vehicle, plenty of hail did hit the COLUMBIA. Some 400 tiles were "dinged" by hailstones during the storm. After a brief evaluation it was decided to roll the rotating service structure back around the vehicle and allow technicians to "spackle" the damaged spots. The results were that after an all-night repair effort, COLUMBIA was deemed ready to fly and there was no delay in the countdown.

STS-4:
LAUNCH OF THE "FORBIDDEN SUBJECT"

What the news media described as "an air of secrecy" supposedly "hung over the mission" due to its highly secret DOD payload that was supposed to be extremely important to national security. Of course if most of us had known what the payload actually was all about, we would have been fairly disappointed. The "forbidden subject" was to never be publically spoken of either during the flight or at any time afterward.

DOD was said to not only be testing the payload, but also the ability to fly secret military payloads on the Space Shuttle. And they got a lesson indeed. Prior to launch, members of the news media managed to dig up the identity of the payload by way of Congressional testimony and inside sources. ABC News' famed spaceflight reporter Jules Bergman even did a pre-launch feature on it, complete with graphics. The package, he said was called "CIRRIS," which stood for Cryogenic InfraRed Radiance Instrumentation for Shuttle. There was also another portion of the package that contained an Ultraviolet Horizon Scanner.

Officially, and secretly, the internal designation of the forbidden subject package was "P82-1," a name that would surely confound those gosh darned Soviets. It was also considered by STS-4's CDR T.K. Mattingly to be "rinky-dink," although he never was able to publically say so until after he retired. In 1982, however, everyone at NASA was doing their best to act like spooks and assure the DOD that they could, in fact, fly secret payloads. Of course all the Soviets had to do was tune in ABC News to get all the information that they needed. Odds are that the KGB already had the inside poop on P82-1, and they probably thought that it was "rinksky dinkski" too.

In absolutely perfect launch weather the countdown neared zero. A silence fell across the causeway as the Space Shuttle Main Engines ignited and turned the pad's water deluge into the now-expected billow of steam. Six seconds later the SRBs ignited and the Florida sun was matched by the brightness of the SRBs. By now, my two buddies and I were veterans of Shuttle launches having witnessed all three of the past missions first hand, but that mattered little. We still screamed like idiots: "GO! GO BABY GO!!" COLUMBIA rolled onto her back and arced into the blue Florida sky like the graceful lady of spaceflight that she was. As her sound rolled over us she again shook us with her magnificence.

We watched SRB "sep" and then did our best to keep our eyes on the white dot that was STS-4 headed for orbit. As always, a glance away and you had lost it from sight. All that was left was to listen to the loop and monitor the progress. People climbed into their cars, but nothing on KSC was allowed to move until the "Negative Return" call was given. Even then, no one was going anyplace. The traffic jam would last well into the afternoon.

While we hung around the car waiting to join the traffic jam, about 125 nautical miles out into the Atlantic the first major failure in the Space Shuttle program was taking place. We did not hear about it until later, when the evening news reported that both of STS-4's SRBs had sunk upon landing. No one seemed to know why, but that did not stop the news media from pointing fingers. The prime target for the finger pointing was the parachutes. One of the foundations of the Shuttle program was the concept of saving money by way of "reusability," and that concept was first exercised on STS-4, which was re-using the SRB parachutes from STS-1. Of course the folks at the Pioneer Parachute Company, who manufactured the parachutes, denied that their canopies were responsible – and they were correct.

What caused the parachute failure was that a new device had been added to the system. The device was a series of explosive charges that were supposed to sever half of the parachute risers when the SRB hit the water. This would allow the canopies to deflate so as to not drag the floating boosters with the wind. Those charges were triggered by "G-switches" that would sense the SRBs hitting the water. Unfortunately, the "G-switches" were set too low and when the frustums (the lower conical portions of the nosecones) that covered the parachutes were jettisoned, the shock of the jettison caused the charges to detonate before the para-chutes ever deployed. As a result, all six parachutes turned into streamers and the high-speed impact with the water caused the booster casings to sink in about 3,000 feet of water. The loss cost the program $58,000,000 plus a lot of needless questions in the news media about the concept of reusability.

STS-4:
PERFORM TAB NOVEMBER

Once in orbit STS-4 pretty much went silent. There was no first-day TV, and few words from the crew, all in the name of DOD secrecy. We all went home and stuck by our radios and TVs in the hope of getting any little tid-bit about the semi-secret, partly DOD mission of STS-4. It would not be until years later that those of us who were space-buffs would find out that the secret mission did not go at all as planned.

For the first four days, their top-secret DOD payload work was causing NASA to keep a tight lid on the mission. Daily press conferences with flight directors were peppered with statements such as, "We can't talk about that." "That's something we can't talk about." "Can't answer that." and of course "No comment." At one point Flight Director Harold Draughon was asked by a reporter if they had ever considered sending up just an empty black box that did nothing and then say they can't talk about it; just to test the secrecy?

"Maybe that's what's in there," Draughon chuckled as he replied.

Oddly, the reporter's question hit close to the truth. The top secret P82-1 payload package, A.K.A. "CIRRIS," actually ended up doing almost nothing other than test the secrecy.

CIRRIS was supposed to be able to sense the heat

signatures of boosting Soviet missiles and provide early warning. One sensor in the package looked for booster exhaust and another was supposed to sense ultraviolet radiation against the earth's horizon. The package, however, had two doors that covered the sensors. During the flight one of the doors failed to open and so that part of the exercise was a complete bust. There is also some debate as to the other part of the package, the Horizon Ultraviolet Program (HUP) experiment, and whether it worked or not. Obscure references indicate that at least some data was gained from the HUP experiment, but it was probably nothing near what DOD had in mind. Thus, instead of a black box that did nothing, the crew of STS-4 ended up with a white package that did... almost nothing.

Of course there could have been more aboard STS-4 than the CIRRIS and that information could still be classified, I will leave that up to the black-projects buffs to discuss.

As another part of the security, the flight crew spoke to a special sort of CAPCOM on the ground as well as the normal CAPCOM in Houston. The special communicator was designated as the "PAYCOM" for Payload Communicator and was located at the National Reconnaissance Office (NRO) in Sunnyvale, California. Most messages from the PAYCOM were spoken in code that referred to a top-secret checklist that was carried aboard the COLUMBIA. The checklist itself was stored in a "safe" which was actually a drawer aboard the orbiter that had a padlock on it. The astronauts unlocked the drawer once in orbit to remove the top-secret checklist and then would be directed by the PAYCOM to select a specific page which would have their next task written on it. Orders would be called up such as "Perform Tab Bravo" and the crew would go to that section of the really secret book and run the procedure. Reading their accounts of the mission you get the impression that the whole exercise became somewhat of a pain for the crew. Finally, after the CIRRIS had fully demonstrated that it was pretty much a flop and that part of the mission appeared to be finished, Hartsfield went down and fully stowed the secret items back into the "safe." It was a task that took a good bit of time and work. That was because items packed in one-G and then unpacked in zero-G have a tendency to not want to fit back into their original space. Finally he finished packing, locked the "safe" and floated up to report to Mattingly that he had finished the task. In his NASA oral history account of the event Hartsfield said that not 20 minutes after he had finished, PAYCOM called and ordered that he "…wanted me to do Tab November." Neither astronaut could recall what Tab November was. So, Hartsfield had to go down, unlock the "safe" and dig out the checklist and flip to "Tab November." That tab said to put everything away, stow the checklist and lock the safe.

STS-4:
LANDING ON JULY 4TH … EVEN
IF IT LAUNCHED ON THE 5TH

Starting on Day 4 the STS-4 mission went back into a near-normal mode for flight testing of the vehicle, as well as a variety of non-secret scientific experiments that needed to be done. Everything from structural heating tests, similar to those done on STS-3, to "plume surveys" took place over the last two full mission days. In all there were 16 scientific tests and 63 vehicle tests that were to be conducted. The biggest disappointment, besides the CIRRIS package, was the Induced Environment Contamination Monitor, which suffered from design flaws and was somewhat of a flop itself. Overall, however, NASA determined post-flight that the STS-4 mission had accomplished 90% of its objectives.

Day 7 was the reentry and landing day and it was all going to take place at Edwards Air Force Base on the Fourth of July holiday. The day was made extra special because President and Mrs. Reagan were to attend the landing. Additionally, NASA used the event to show off the newest orbiter in the fleet: the CHALLENGER. She was atop the 747 Shuttle Carrier Aircraft (SCA) and scheduled to depart shortly after the COLUMBIA arrived. (See Image 13, page 78.)

"… they wanted to make sure that we landed on the fourth of July." Mattingly later recalled laughingly, "It was no uncertain terms that we were going to land on the fourth of July, no matter what day we took off. Even if it was the fifth, we were going to land on the fourth. That meant, if you didn't do any of your test mission, that's okay, as long as we landed on the fourth, because the President is going to be there."

He went on to explain that the crew had met for lunch with the NASA administrator the day before launch day and the administrator made sure to remind them to have something to say for the President after they landed.

"We never came up with something we could say," Mattingly recalled, "but we came up with a whole lot of humor that we didn't dare say."

Reentry went normally as did most of the approach, but later Mattingly's luck would change a little bit for the worst. Unlike STS-3, this profile was similar to those that would be flown on future operational missions. Mattingly, like all Shuttle CDRs since the first free-flight test of the ENTERPRISE, was intending to allow Hartsfield fly a portion of the Heading Alignment Circle (HAC). As Mattingly intercepted the HAC and began the turn he turned his head toward Hartsfield preparing to say "...okay, here, take it for a bit..." He recalled that at that instant;

"...suddenly my (sense of balance) gyros tumbled and I just had the worse case of vertigo I've ever had. Broad daylight. It was really overwhelming."

Instinctively, he went back onto his instruments and rebalanced his senses by focusing there.

Puzzled, Hartsfield asked, "Are you gonna let me fly?"

"No, no," Mattingly simply responded, "I can't talk about it now."

Later he would explain to his PLT what had happened. No doubt Hartsfield understood fully, as any professional pilot would. The landing turned into a greaser, in fact both astronauts were unsure if the wheels had actually contacted the runway, but there they were rolling along. Hartsfield had to remind Mattingly to go ahead and put the nose down.

"I'd never been able to do that again in any airplane. Never did it before," Mattingly later recalled.

Once the COLUMBIA had fully stopped and the final checklists were completed, the two astronauts removed their helmets and tried to get out of their seats. Both found it excessively difficult to move. A full week in zero-G was allowing gravity to take its revenge upon them. Mattingly seemed to be suffering from it the worst as he struggled to get up out of his seat. Finally, frustration took over and he just pushed up as hard as he could. The effort cost him. As he regained his ability to stand, he drove himself head-first, minus his helmet, into the overhead panel and suffering a cut as a result.

"…blood was coming out," He later recalled, "it was terrible. Oh, did I have a headache."

To make matters worse, the person waiting for him at the bottom of the stairs would be President Reagan. Of course, Mattingly got it all together before the two Shuttle pilots left the orbiter and met the President in front of the TV cameras. Those of us watching at home that day saw the crew come out, meet the President and First Lady, and do a short walk-around the COLUMBIA. Mrs. Reagan did what any of us would have done if given the chance. She walked over and touched the orbiter.

Later in the day, President Reagan gave a speech about our nation's future in space, with the orbiter ENTERPRISE as a backdrop. Although some in NASA were disappointed that he did not announce a new space station, he spoke in specific terms about the Shuttle and declared the STS to be "Fully operational." Shortly thereafter he made the call that the CHALLENGER, which had been in position and holding at the end of the runway was "…free to take off now!" With that, Fitz Fulton put the throttles on the SCA forward and the spacecraft and her 747 mother ship majestically began to roll as the crowd cheered. Next the STS-4 crew said a few words. Mattingly, a man of few words in public, made a very profound comment that captured the exact mood at that moment in history. He said about the Shuttles, in part,

"…the machine we built (the COLUMBIA) is the first stepping stone. Here comes the second one (pointing toward CHALLENGER), we're standing in front of its pathfinder (the ENTERPRISE) and there's more to come."

The SCA roared past as the crowd cheered and screamed.

Indeed there WAS more to come. After seeing our nation's space program wither at the end of Apollo, after watching space program critics from Capitol Hill to the news media call for the outright cancellation of the Shuttle, after seeing the Kennedy Space Center turned into little more than a side-trip after a visit to Disney World, there was the very real feeling that WE WERE BACK in space. And now, with our magnificent Shuttle machines, we Americans would lead the world in spaceflight from this day forward.

Following Mattingly and Hartsfield's speeches, President Reagan returned to the microphone. He said a few parting words and then, as the SCA came around for a low pass, the band (Yes, there was a band there; after all it was the Fourth of July holiday.) was cued to strike up "God Bless America." President Reagan began to sing (without a teleprompter... ahem) "God Bless America," and the entire crowd, including the STS-4 crew, joined in. Reagan, being a former actor, was a good singer too and he just rolled along singing and proudly smiling as the CHALLENGER and SCA passed by. It gives you shivers to watch that on video more than three decades later.

What a time that was for spaceflight. The Soviets were launching Soyuz rockets at the rate of nearly two a week, we had an operational Shuttle on the runway and another on the SCA headed for KSC, plus two more in the barn getting ready to fly. NASA was talking about 30 flights a year in the decade ahead and the US Air Force was constructing their own Shuttle pad at Vandenberg Air Force Base in California. It was an exciting time, no doubt.

After the SCA passed, the President turned to the STS-4 crew and said, "That could puddle you up."

He was right, it was a scene that made your spirit soar as the TV screen was filled with the silver 747, with its red, white and blue stripes proudly flying by with America's newest space shuttle on its back. It all seemed to say what the President had highlighted in his speech, reminding the nation that we Americans can do anything, because "we're a prosperous people, we're a strong people, because we're a FREE people." He then concluded the event by saying to the crowd and to the nation,

"Happy Fourth of July and you know this has got to beat firecrackers."

The crowd went nuts.

Even though at that time I was just a college student, working my way through school by earning minimum wage at the Daytona Kmart store's garden shop, loading bags of pine bark nuggets and cow manure and living like a college kid, I felt the same as the folks in that crowd. Watching the events surrounding the STS-4 landing, I was proud to be an American at that moment.

Fast-forward to later that afternoon as my bottle rocket Shuttle rocketed through the tree canopy above our Holly Hill, Florida, front yard and popped somewhere overhead in an apparently destructive fireworks report. My two pals were roaring with drunken laughter. One doubled over and the other fell on the ground. I, however, being the long time model rocket flyer, instinctively scanned the trees in the hope that some pieces may drop through.

Then, suddenly, through the hole in the tree canopy that I had been aiming for, but missed at launch, my little orbiter came gliding as if being piloted by T. K. Mattingly himself.

"Check this out!" I shouted, pointing at the little orbiter.

For a second we all sort of froze there in amazement as the orbiter flew past us overhead, made a wide, graceful right hand turn and then flew directly over us again and landed in the yard next door; as pretty as can be. There was a moment of "NO WAY!" gasping and then both of my drunken pals were on the ground rolling with amazed laughter. I trotted over giggling in amazement and brought my orbiter back in the palm of my hand. I never did find any of the booster parts, but I kept the orbiter and still have it. As I said before, it is a tribute to my insanity as well as an artifact of my growing up with spaceflight.

STS-5
WHO COULD BE EXCITED ABOUT
A TRUCKING COMPANY?

To someone who had been growing up with space-flight the fact that life had taken me to within a 40 minute driving distance of the Kennedy Space Center seemed like a blessing indeed. The fact that life also had deposited me in the Daytona Beach Kmart store as an employee for the past two years and equipped me with nothing more than a 10-speed bicycle for transportation, however, clearly demonstrated that God does have a sense of humor. Still, when it came to launch of STS-5, it all seemed to just work out for me. Oddly, my venture to see the STS-5 launch began with a series of other people's misfortunes.

As I was doing my best to work my way back into college by saving the lawns and gardens of Volusia County while toiling in the Kmart garden shop a few days before the launch, I was stopped on the way to my lunch break by one of the other employees.

"You always go to those Shuttle launches don't ya'?" he asked me.

I replied that I did and he explained that he had scored a vehicle pass for the causeway, but the transmission had just dropped out of his car. He asked if I knew anyone else who wanted to go down for the launch that had a working car and may be willing to drive him and his pass to KSC. I told him I would do my best to make that connection if I could. The following day I was hanging out in the Embry-Riddle Aeronautical University's student newspaper office. My cartoon strips were always running in the Avion newspaper, so my status was always that of being a part of the staff no matter if I was currently enrolled in the school or not. Sometime during the day my pal "Cheff Spaghetti," who had been with me at the STS-2 launch and who was also a charter member of the L-5 Aerospace Society, ambled into the office grumbling about the launch. It seemed that the gang at L-5 could get a university van to travel down to the STS-5 launch, but they were unable to get a vehicle pass. Of course it took me about 90 seconds to close that deal. I could provide their pass if they would reserve two seats on the van; one for me and one for the guy with the pass.

Deal!

So it was that in the pre-dawn darkness of Thursday, November 11, 1982, some 11 of us climbed aboard one of the powder blue and white ERAU vans and headed off to see STS-5. Finding my seat in the stretched van, the thought struck me that just 17 months earlier, in April of 1981, I was unable to get a seat aboard either one of the two big tour busses that were headed down from the university for STS-1. Now here we were, a year and a half later, and the sum total of us willing to sacrifice a school day to see the Shuttle fly was 11 people, including the van driver, who was a faculty member. It seemed to indicate a drastic decline in interest.

Of course, such a decline in the excitement over the Space Shuttle was exactly what NASA was seeking with STS-5. For years the space agency had quipped that its goal was to make Space Shuttle flights so common and routine that one day the press would not even bother to cover them. In my opinion, such a goal was so contrary to the essence of human spaceflight that it was pure fiction. Likewise the bold statements that the Shuttle would one day financially "break even," and eventually actually earn a profit by hauling commercial satellites into orbit also was a myth. This all was rooted in a projected flight rate that was impossible to achieve with almost any space vehicle. Yet this was the song that NASA was forced to sing in order to sell the Shuttle to the myopic politicians who held the purse strings. Thus, STS-5 was being portrayed as the first commercial use of the Space Shuttle. The moniker "Ace Trucking Company" was happily applied to the mission and the Shuttle by NASA management. After all, who could have much interest in a trucking company? Frankly, I believe that this sort of tinting of the program was an early mistake on NASA's part. Once public interest is doused, it is nearly impossible to re-kindle.

As we approached KSC in our school van, the line-up to get to the space center, although far from the STS-1 crowds, was quite similar to that of STS-4. Traffic was not jammed, however, and we simply kept rolling steadily along up to and through the gate. Again, the parking on the causeway had cars stacked door-to-door 6 to 14 deep. The loud speakers were set up and broadcasting the launch control "loop" and all appeared ready for the launch. As the sun came up, it revealed perhaps one of the finest days ever seen for a Shuttle launch. We all spread out and listened to the loop.

Aboard STS-5 was the largest crew ever launched; a total of four astronauts. In command was a veteran as-tronaut of the Apollo Soyuz Test Project (ASTP), Vance Brand. His PLT was space rookie Bob Overmyer, who had come to NASA in 1969 from the top secret MOL project.

Flying along for the first time were two "Mission Specialists." Dr. Bill Lenoir, an electrical engineer would ride into orbit up on the flight deck. Meanwhile, Dr. Joe Allen had to ride down on the mid-deck, "stuck down in steerage," for the launch. This arrangement would be switched on reentry, however, and Lenoir would be stuck in steerage while Allen would ride up on the flight deck. Joe Allen had become a favorite of many space-buffs, including myself, when he did an amazing job as the CAPCOM during the extended Apollo 15 lunar EVAs.

One of the interesting aspects of my experiences in those early Shuttle days was that because I was there to see the first seven launches in person, aside from STS-1 and some of STS-3 where we had a TV with us on the riverbank, I never got to see them on TV. Although I had witnessed almost all of Mercury, Gemini, Apollo, Skylab and ASTP on television, I had missed five of the first seven Shuttle broadcasts. Today, thanks to YouTube, I have been able to fill that void.

Coverage for the STS-5 launch would have made NASA's upper management quite happy. With the exception of one network, every TV news network in the United States began coverage around the time that the count came out of the nine minute hold. ABC news broke into "Good Morning America" for its STS-5 coverage. But then they broke away so that host David Hartman could talk about the death of Soviet leader Leonid Brezhnev with former President Jimmy Carter. The TV audience, however, were mercifully spared that torment because the sound failed at Carter's end and all that could be heard was launch control in the background instead of Carter. The one network that actually was refining and expanding its coverage in those days was CNN. Of course with their new all-news, all-the-time format, they needed content. The Shuttle served that purpose quite well. Thus, through the entire STS-5 mission, every time the crew had a TV downlink going it was being broadcast on CNN while the other networks simply ran their usual soap operas and game shows.

STS-5 was slated to launch two satellites. Additionally, astronauts Allen and Lenoir were scheduled to do the first US EVA since Skylab in 1974. Still, it was the release of the satellites that NASA was really promoting. The COMSATs were being launched for TELESAT Canada and Satellite Business Systems. The first release would take place on flight day number one, the second on flight day number two and the EVA would take place on flight day number four. Five flight days were scheduled with reentry and landing supposed to take place early on day number six.

In yet another attempt to make Shuttle flying appear commonplace, the pressure suits worn on previous Shuttle launches were now done away with and replaced by regular NASA flight suits, as well as helmets that could easily be mistaken for motorcycle head gear, yet probably afforded less protection. All of this was a part of the "new" operational era of spaceflight. Even if the mission was just as dangerous as every other spaceflight, it would, at least, look commonplace.

As the count continued, not a single flaw was touched upon. The causeway erupted in screams, whistles, cheers and rebel yells as the main engines ignited and came up to speed.

At liftoff the Shuttle did not disappoint the crowd. Every Shuttle launch seemed like it was the first one that you had experienced. It was clear that no matter how hard NASA tried, no Shuttle launch would ever be as commonplace as a truck. It was always something that reaches out, takes hold of you and thunders against your skin. You could not simply hear it- you had to feel it too. STS-5 climbed into a clear blue Florida sky, but the crew said very little other than making the standard required calls. At SRB separation the expended solids could be seen tumbling away for a protracted period. Soon, however, they were lost from sight. Although we thought of them as "falling" away, their inertia actually kept them traveling upward in the near vacuum of the upper atmosphere and downrange. Separation generally took place at about 154,000 feet, but they continued climbing to about 230,000 feet of altitude before actually beginning to fall back toward earth. STS-5 made orbit just fine even though the SRBs had produced a slightly depressed trajectory. We piled back into the van, and joined the crowd trying to leave KSC and await the next launch of a Space Shuttle. Everyone was sure that just like the next truck or train passing by, there would always be a next Shuttle launch roaring into the Florida sky. It is a part of the human condition to see the future as bright against present glory. (See Image 14, page 78.)

STS-5:
AS LITTLE FANFARE AS NASA
COULD MUSTER

Shortly after we had returned to Daytona, the crew of STS-5 was preparing to release the first of their two satellites. Each satellite was contained in a cradle which was covered with a retractable sun-shield. The satellite itself was mounted to a solid rocket motor called a Payload Assist Module (PAM) which was seated upon a turn-table like device called a "spin table." A command from the orbiter's aft work station caused the sun-shield to open. Another command signaled the spin table to begin rotating. The spinning action imparted stability into the satellite as it moved clear and was later boosted into its proposed orbit. This rotation could be between 45 rpm and 100 rpm depending on the needs of the satellite.

For STS-5's satellites a rate of 50 rpm was required. A "Marman clamp" held the satellite onto the spin table against a spring secured by explosive bolts. When the proper time came, a command was sent to detonate the bolts and the spinning satellite was ejected from the cargo bay of the Shuttle at a rate of three feet per second. The orbiter was then moved to a distance of 16 miles from the satellite. A timer aboard the satellite and PAM combination fired the solid rocket motor 45 minutes after it had left the spin-table and boosted it to its desired orbit. Both satellites were successfully deployed. The Satellite Business Systems unit was deployed at 3:17 pm EST on flight day one and the TELESAT Canada unit was deployed 3:24 pm EST on day two. As a result, the crew took on the motto, "We Deliver."

After the second satellite was ejected, two of the crew-members were struck by a case of space adaptation sickness, a type of motion sickness that is only found to strike people in micro gravity. Hardcore test pilots and mission specialists alike can be hit by it. In the case of STS-5, Bob Overmyer, a tough Marine pilot, and Bill Lenoir, a PhD. Engineer, were both struck for what remained of day two. By day three, Overmyer was feeling fine, but Lenoir was still not 100%. The scheduled EVA was postponed.

Later, the EVA was cancelled, not due to space sickness, but due to issues with the suits. While in preparation for the EVA, Joe Allen discovered that his suit's circulating fan was not functioning properly. The fan would start up, run for a short time and then stop. While protracted trouble-shooting from the ground was taking place on that glitch, Lenoir discovered that his suit was also not function-ing correctly. It was regulating at 3.6 PSI rather than the expected 4.3 PSI. More trouble-shooting could not solve the problems and the EVA was eventually scrubbed.

STS-5:
GONE WERE THE DAYS

I managed to swap shifts with one of my fellow lawn, pine bark and cow manure technicians at the Kmart garden shop on flight day six so I could be home that morning and watch STS-5 land. That landing was done at Edwards AFB and was planned to take place at 9:26 am EST, Tuesday, November 16. Gone were the days when the networks started coverage of the landing prior to de-orbit burn. This time the networks picked up coverage about 19 minutes prior to touchdown. Edwards was forecast to have a scattered layer of clouds with bottoms around 16,000 AGL, but as the sun came up it was obvious that the layer had turned to a near overcast. John Young, flying the STA, reported the conditions as being "marginal."

Vance Brand was going to have an interesting approach on his hands. He was going to drop like a lead sled into an overcast layer and hope that all of NASA's data had been correct and there would be a runway on the other side. Of course pilots had been doing these dive-bomber approaches since the M2-F1 lifting body flights during the early 1960s. Vance himself had done countless such approaches during training in the Shuttle Training Aircraft and T-38, so there was no real abnormal risk involved. It's just kind of fun to think that he was just a little bit puckered on this one.

ABC News had hired Gene Cernan to assist and do "color" commentary during all of these very early Shuttle missions. In my opinion, they struck gold. Cernan was not only a national hero, having flown a Gemini mission and two Apollo missions, as well as having been the last human ever to stand on the surface of the moon, but he was a natural when it came to broadcasting spaceflights. During the early Shuttle missions you wanted to superglue your dial to ABC for launches and landings just to watch Cernan.

This time the COLUMBIA popped through the overcast right on target and slid down the glide-slope as pretty as could be. Setting smoothly down on Runway 22, she rolled to a stop in a routine that would become so familiar that indeed one day the big networks would not bother to cover it live. This time they at least cut back later to show us the crew coming down the stairs and then that was that. The first operational, commercial flight of the Shuttle was over with as little fanfare as NASA could muster.

I rode my bicycle to work that afternoon thinking that this program was rapidly going the way of Skylab, with the media losing interest and the public doing the same. Only this time it appeared as if that was exactly NASA's intention. However, as long as I was living in Daytona at least I would always get to see the launches live in spite of the media's lack of interest. The Space Shuttle was a big success and I felt certain that it would fly for the rest of my life. Of course, I was wrong.

STS-6
A HUGE GLASS OF ICED TEA AND
BOX OF BLUEBERRY POP TARTS

As astronaut Story Musgrave cracked open the exterior hatch of the orbiter's airlock, he drew it in toward himself. Once the hatch was angled over and stowed he moved slowly out into the open cargo bay. It was the beginning of America's first spacewalk since 1974; nine years, two months and three days earlier.

"It's a little deeper pool than I'm used to working in," Musgrave quipped, looking at the blue Earth below him.

His reference was a comparison to the neutral buoyancy tanks in which he had been training to simulate micro gravity. Back in 1974, no one outside of NASA bothered to pick up and rebroadcast the Skylab EVA as it was transmitted from a single camera. On STS-6, there were four cameras mounted in the cargo bay of the orbiter and every news outlet was carrying every bit of video that was beamed down from the Shuttle. I sat, mesmerized, in front of my TV set with a huge glass of iced tea and box of blueberry pop tarts. My growing up with spaceflight luck was working out nicely as the EVA took place on my scheduled day off from my new job at a beach-side hotel. Life was good for a space-buff.

STS-6:
CHALLENGER COMES TO LIFE

It had been a long wait to get the Shuttle CHALLENGER and STS-6 off the pad. CHALLENGER had arrived at KSC on July 5, 1982, after its christening flight from Edwards Air Force Base in front of President Regan the previous day. The new orbiter was transported into the Orbiter Processing Facility the following day and the task of making it ready to launch was started. Meanwhile the SRBs were stacked on the Mobile Launch Platform (MLP) over the first two weeks of October and the External Tank was mated with the boosters a week later on October 21.

Lighter weight and greater power were supposed to be two of the hallmarks for STS-6. The SRBs were sporting new lightweight cases that shaved approximately 4,000 pounds off of the SRBs flown on the five previous missions. Likewise, the ET had been placed on a diet and shaved about 10,000 pounds off of its weight. To achieve the reduction in ET weight, portions of the vertical "stringers" that ran the length of the hydrogen tank were deleted, and a lot of the other structural materials were milled differently so as to reduce their weight while not reducing their strength. Moreover, a stronger, yet lighter and less expensive titanium alloy was used in the tank's aft SRB attachments. Lastly, the CHALLENGER's SSMEs were the first to be flown with the capability to throttle-up to 104% of their rated thrust.

Although these engines had accumulated a total of 45,000 seconds of test firing time, once they were placed on the CHALLENGER they would turn into a real nightmare.

A thick ground fog covered Launch Complex 39 on November 30 as the STS-6 stack was rolled out from the VAB to Pad 39A. The scene was quite surreal, with just the upper portion of the VAB, the two Fixed Service Structures at the pads and the launch vehicle sticking up through the fog. In spite of the fog the rollout was accomplished without a hint of trouble.

A Flight Readiness Firing (FRF) of the CHALLENGER's SSMEs was later conducted on December 18, and that was when the fun began. Although the burn went as planned, test equipment located in the orbiter's boat-tail sensed an abnormally high presence of hydrogen gas present in the engine compartment's internal areas. At first it was thought that the hydrogen gas was coming from an external source, perhaps a small leak caused by the vibration of the static firing. Inspection found there was a small leak near the rim of one of the three SSMEs. That area was patched and a second FRF was scheduled. As a result, the original January 20, 1983, launch date for the CHALLENGER went down the drain.

By the time that the second FRF took place I had liberated myself from laboring for minimum wage at Kmart and moved over to laboring for minimum wage at one of the beachside hotels in Daytona. My new job prohibited me from getting down to KSC to witness the FRF, but I did manage to get an entire ballroom carpet cleaned that day. Meanwhile, down at KSC, the Shuttle launch team was having far less success with the CHALLENGER.

The second FRF saw the orbiter packed with a lot more sensors in case the hydrogen leak reappeared.

Those sensor readings showed a similar gathering of hydrogen in the aft section once more. This time NASA conducted an extensive and revised series of leak checks on the CHALLENGER's SSMEs. Ground crews discovered that there was a leak in a weld on the tubing leading to engine number one's combustion chamber. Subsequently, that engine was removed and replaced with the backup engine. Upon arriving at KSC, the backup engine itself was found to have a leak in its heat exchanger. A third engine was ordered from the National Space Technologies Laboratories in Mississippi. That engine was required to make a full duration static firing on the test stand for 500 seconds before being sent to KSC. After it was installed everything seemed to be in order for the upcoming launch.

I managed to luck out once again, as the April 4 launch date for STS-6 fell on my scheduled day off from work. Thus, again the trio of space-buffs who had witnessed STS-1, and STS-4 – Brian, Jennings and myself – joined together to go down and cheer a Shuttle launch off the pad. We really did not have any idea that this would be the final time that all three of us would witness a launch together. In the months and years ahead we all would be swept in different directions by the winds of life. On April 4, 1983, however, we were all for one and one for all as we again passed through KSC security on our way to the causeway, minus the fake Russian accents, of course.

Most of the folks who were there to see the launch of STS-6 had no idea that many in the firing room were apprehensive about the new engines and CHALLENGER's ride up-hill. In fact much of the crowd consisted of local folks who now knew very well how to get vehicle passes. Across the river in Titusville, however, the story was a bit different. It was Spring Break on Florida's East Coast and hordes of college kids had ventured down from Daytona or up from Fort Lauderdale to see the Shuttle launch. The streets were lined with college kids and news reports estimated that the crowd number was near that of STS-1.

In yet another change from the previous Shuttle launches, STS-6 was scheduled to liftoff at 1:30 in the afternoon. Thus, there was no all-night vigil and no middle of the night trek down to KSC. Brian, Jennings and I had actually headed down from Daytona around breakfast time and leisurely made our way onto the space center. The countdown for STS-6 also went off in the same leisurely manner. As the CHALLENGER ignited so did your soul and everyone who was able to lay eyes upon Pad 39A turned into a screaming, whistling, cheering space-buff. Your brain simply overloaded and every one of your senses became focused on the ascending Shuttle. It did not matter if you were a spring-breaker seeing your first launch, or someone like me who had seen every single one of the Shuttle launches, you were simply captivated. You hardly noticed the world around you; the Shuttle had your complete attention at that time and it held onto you. STS-6 launched into a crystal clear Florida sky and we easily watched it all the way up to SRB separation and then a bit beyond.

Once the Shuttle was lost from sight the thought struck me that I had been able to witness every single Shuttle launch so far while standing somewhere on the Space Coast. Six manned launches in just two years; man was I lucky. I considered how many other die-hard space-buffs had never witnessed any sort of launch other than through their TV set. I joked with Brian and Jennings that we three should get T-shirts made saying we had witnessed the launches. Of course, we were all so broke that no such thing could ever be done.

STS-6:
"IT'S ALL COMING TOGETHER"

On its first day in orbit STS-6 was scheduled to launch the first in a series of Tracking and Data Relay Satellites (TDRS). These satellites would form a network in geosynchronous orbit that would eliminate the need of NASA to communicate with Shuttles by way of intermittent ground stations. The "launch" method of the huge satellite was by way of a solid propellant Inertial Upper Stage (IUS). The two stage IUS was a concept that had come along early in the planning for the Shuttle system. It was fit into a launch ring, called a "Tilt Table" and was elevated to an attitude of 29 degrees up from the orbiter's longitudinal plane, and later 59 degrees in the orbiter's cargo bay and then ejected by springs. The orbiter then backed away about 32 miles from the stage and when the IUS ignited it was supposed to drive the TRDS into an orbit of about 22,400 miles high. Although the deployment from the shuttle itself was flawless, the IUS malfunctioned and dumped the TDRS in an orbit that was far lower than required. Over the following months, controllers on the ground were able to use the satellite's reaction control thrusters to stabilize it and eventually boost it into its assigned orbit.

Then came Thursday, April 7, and the first US spacewalk in nearly a decade. Oddly, some Internet sites say that the EVA took place on April 8, yet my tapes from the mission, plus NASA documents, plus the simple fact that my days off back then were Monday, Wednesday and Thursday, all indicate that the EVA took place on the Thursday the 7th. At least one Internet source tries to fudge it by saying that the four hour EVA took place on "April 7-8." I guess it's hard to be wrong if you just spread it over two days. On the actual day of the EVA I suddenly found that space suits were no longer called "space suits," they were now "Extra-vehicular Mobility Units," or EMU's. NASA said that the name was reasoned from the fact that these suits had been so refined that they were actually spaceflight vehicles onto themselves. My bet was that it came from the Shuttle program's inability to simply call anything what it actually is and instead develop an acronym. Thus, for Extra-vehicular Maneuvering Unit we have EMU because the acronym for Astronaut Space Suit would be… well, you get the idea.

(See Image 15, page 78.) Story Musgrave made his way from the airlock and out into the expanse of the CHALLENGER's payload bay. Following immediately came Don Peterson and for the next four hours and 15 minutes they set the foundation for Shuttle EVAs for the next three decades. Interestingly, there was probably more network TV coverage of this one EVA than had been allotted all of the Skylab EVAs a decade earlier. Musgrave even took the extra time to go up toward the OMS pod and inspect some thermal blanketing that had come loose during ascent. His fellow astronauts said that Musgrave had been tinkering with and tweaking the EMUs for months. They were "his babies" and Story was making sure, first hand, that nothing would go wrong with the suits. As a result, the EMUs functioned nearly flawlessly and both astronauts returned to the orbiter in great shape. Musgrave would go on to, at one point in the program, hold the record for the most hours spent outside of Shuttles on EVAs. Eventually he would see that record surpassed, yet he would gain another record that could never be surpassed. On November 19, 1996, Story Musgrave would become the only person to fly on all five of the Shuttle orbiters as he was launched aboard COLUMBIA for mission STS-80.

De-orbit of the CHALLENGER began on the morning of Saturday, April 9, 1983. My luck for being off work for Shuttle events, however, seemed to be running out. By the time that the CHALLENGER was making her approach to Runway 22 at Edwards Air Force Base, I would be at work inventorying bottles of booze for the hotel's three nightclubs. After all, it was spring break and more booze was being consumed in Daytona Beach than LOX and LH2 were consumed on STS-6, so I had my work cut out for me. Of course I was not about to miss recording the landing. So, before I left the house I placed my tape recorder in front of my TV, turned the set on ABC and told my roommate to go in there and hit the "record" button at 1:30 in the afternoon, which was about 23 minutes before the scheduled touchdown of the orbiter. My instructions then were to just let the tape run out. Of course like all roommates who have zero interest in spaceflight, my roommate was 12 minutes tardy in pushing the button. It really did not matter because I did capture the landing and plenty of other coverage. Frankly, I felt lucky that my roommate remembered at all.

Once the mission was completed and the crew of STS-6 had returned home to Houston where NASA arranged a news conference. A movie of the mission was shown and narrated by the crew led by CDR Paul Weitz. The components of the Space Transportation System were all starting to work together— from the EMUs to the orbiter's toilets. With the CHALLENGER online NASA could now boast that they had a "fleet" of Shuttles, even if it was just a two-orbiter fleet. Turn-around time of the Shuttles between missions was getting shorter and mission times were being protracted. Overall, confidence in the entire program was rapidly growing. As Weitz closed the post-mission news conference he simply stated, "It's all comin' together."

STS-7
ALMOST ROUTINE

STS-7 would be the first Shuttle launch that I would not get to see from the space coast. Just two-and-a-half hours after liftoff I had to be at work to earn my minimum wage inventorying the "liquor room" at a beachside hotel. Being the only non-drinker that I think they ever had on staff, I was the only person they could trust to be locked in that room full of booze for five hours and not get soused. In fact they had fired a half dozen guys before they tried me and were a bit amazed when I did what they were paying me to do: inventory the bottles of booze for the nightclubs. Thus, instead of watching the launch from the causeway at KSC on Saturday, June 18, 1983, I would be forced to watch this one closer to the house where I was living in Ormond Beach.

I had done some pre-launch "recon" and decided to watch from the Granada Avenue Bridge, a local high-rise span with a clear view of the horizon when looking toward the Cape. It took me about 12 minutes to peddle my bike from my house to the peak of the bridge, including the time to get my bike out the front door. That meant I would have to gamble on the countdown coming successfully out of the T-9 minute hold. My plan was to start my ever-present tape recorder in front of my TV at 14 minutes prior to the scheduled launch time and ride as fast as I could to the bridge. With any luck there may be someone else at the bridge with a radio so we could keep track of the count. If nothing got in my way and if no senior citizen ran me over with their car, I figured that I just might make it.

Growing up with spaceflight, you learn to plan for contingencies. Of course, getting run over by some old fart who believes that bike lanes are their own senior citizens driving lanes is really hard to plan around.

Pre-launch coverage started quite early for this flight and at the calculated time, I hit my tape recorder, bolted out the door and leaped upon my trusty bicycle to ride like a lunatic. I could have felt sorry for that little old lady walking her poodle that morning, but it was her fault for being on the bike path.

Launch coverage was huge for STS-7 as compared to the previous flight and there was one big reason for that: her name was Sally Ride. Indeed this was to be the mission that would loft the first American female astronaut and although I thought that it was simply a natural progression in the program, the news media clearly though it was a real big deal. Female broadcasters who you would normally never see covering a Shuttle launch, or any other sort of space launch, were now on the TV talking as if they actually had a clue about spaceflight. Jane Pauley, who probably did not know hypergolic from hypersonic, was at the desk broadcasting live from the KSC Press site for NBC. The atmosphere on the networks seemed almost festive. There were, of course, the accounts of the Soviets having flown females in space and the predictable questions as to why it had taken so long for the United States to get a female into space. It was obvious that the people asking those questions had absolutely no insight as to the details of how previous Mercury, Gemini and Apollo crews had gone to the bathroom in space. Anyone actually familiar with that process would never have asked why NASA had to wait until the Shuttle to get a female astronaut into space. In all previous NASA spacecraft the astronauts pooped into blue plastic bags and peed into an overboard hose system by way of a device similar to a condom; the Shuttle, however, was equipped with a unisex toilet.

(See Image 16, page 79.) Peddling for all I was worth, I arrived at the Granada Avenue bridge exactly as planned. To my amazement there was a huge crowd of Shuttle watchers lining the south side of the bridge. We all stood there together and watched and applauded as STS-7 appeared on the southern horizon and climbed into space. Although watching a Shuttle launch live from anyplace was both a thrill and a privilege I decided they were always better seen from the Space Coast. Getting back to my house I found that the network coverage of the launch had already ended. Apparently once the Shuttle was out of sight, so was the story.

STS-7
"RIDE SALLY RIDE"

When I got to work on launch day, and once again found myself locked in the "liquor room," I had a lot of time to think as I unsealed and resealed scores of booze bottles and inventoried each one. I was impressed by the crowd at the bridge who had showed up in spite of NASA's insistence that soon the Shuttle missions would one day launch so frequently that they would become "almost routine." I had hoped that such would never become the case. My hope was reinforced later that day when I got onto one of the hotel elevators. As I reached up to push the button, I saw that someone had scrolled on the wall, apparently in female handwriting, three words: "Ride Sally Ride."

Orbital Vehicle 99, the CHALLENGER, went about her mission as routinely as NASA could have wished. Two satellites were deployed: the ANIK C-2 for TELESAT Canada and the PALAPA-B1 for Indonesia. Both satellites were boosted by Payload Assist Module-D motors and worked as advertised. One of the primary experiments aboard STS-7 was the Scientific Pallet Satellite 01, or "SPAS-01." No one bothered to ask where the extra "A" in the acronym came from. It had all sorts of instrumentation, including one for forming metal alloys in microgravity, along with nine other tests. My personal favorite was the Getaway Special experiment that took a colony of ants aloft to study their behavior in microgravity. Odds are that somewhere out there is a PhD. thesis based on that experiment whose point is, "Floated around and looked confused a lot," but uses 20,000 really big words to say it.

Landing for STS-7 was planned for KSC, but the weather would not allow it. Thus the landing was waved off for two orbits and re-targeted for Edwards Air Force Base. CDR Bob Crippen hand-flew the orbiter in for his first actual Shuttle landing, having only momentarily held the controls on STS-1. After being selected for the MOL he had waited 15 years to get his first space flight, now, in just 26 months he had flown twice in space. Touching down on runway 15, the bird rolled out for 10,450 feet. Shortly thereafter, Crippen, along with PLT Fred Hauck, mission specialists John Fabian, Norm Thagard and Sally Ride, came down the air-stairs and concluded the mission in an almost routine manner.

BACK TO WATCHING ON TV

A little over a month after STS-7 landed, I left Florida to return to my home state of Michigan in order to more effectively earn money for college. Over the next year I would have to revert back to watching the launches on TV as four more Shuttle flights went into orbit. I do not know which I longed to do more, go back to Florida and watch Shuttle launches or return to Florida and continue my own flight training. Still, although not able to experience the flights in person I was able to watch like the rest of the country as the first "African-American" astronaut, Guy Bluford, flew on STS-8, and as the first six-man crew flew on STS-9.

On the tenth mission those of us in the hard-core space-buff community collectively cheered as Bruce McCandless flew the Manned Maneuvering Unit (MMU) on the world's first un-tethered EVA. McCandless had spent most of his early NASA career working on the M-509 version of the MMU, which he co-designed. Later he was dedicated to the development of the Hughes 376 model MMU used on the Shuttle. It could easily be said that the MMU was Bruce's baby- so it was justice that he should be the test pilot to fly it in space for the first time. As I watched him fly out of the CHALLENGER's cargo bay, I recalled whispering, "Go Bruce," to myself.

(See Image 17, page 79.) On the 11th Shuttle mission the crew captured and repaired a satellite in space for the first time. Even with all of that going on, it began to appear that NASA was getting its wish. Shuttle missions were starting to be seen by the general public as being "almost routine."

Computer and engine troubles delayed the maiden flight of the orbiter DISCOVERY on the 12th Shuttle mission for just over two months, much to my approval. By that time I had resolved my financial issues and was back in Daytona Beach at Embry-Riddle as a full-time flight student. I had arrived on campus just in time to watch DISCOVERY. Even I had found myself slipping into the "almost routine" delusion. By now I had my own flying career in my sights and, being focused upon it, I simply could not allow myself to get too distracted from school to continue vicariously chasing spacecraft. That 12th Shuttle launch was the first flight that I had not taped since Apollo 14. I simply watched as DISCOVERY arced into the blue Florida sky that Thursday morning, and as soon as the SRBs separated I hustled on to my Global Navigation class. "Almost routine," indeed.

STS-61A:
NO ONE KNEW WHAT THE
HELL HAPPENED TO 41E

By the time I got back to college full-time, in the autumn of 1984, the Space Shuttle program was rolling along at full steam. The year 1984 would see five Shuttle missions launched and 1985 would nearly double that tally with nine missions launched. Of course this was nowhere near 50 plus launches per year that NASA had entered the program boasting of, but the growing flight rate was impressive to anyone following the program. Likewise the Embry-Riddle student newspaper, the Avion, of which I was a staff member, was now heavily into the Shuttle, having added a "Space Technology" section and assigned it an editor. It was good to be back at school and it was a good time to be on the Avion staff, even if I was only the cartoonist.

Starting in 1984 with the 10th launch of the Shuttle, NASA headquarters had passed down a mandate that all future Shuttle flights were to be re-designated. No longer would there be a logical STS-10, 11, 12, or heaven forbid 13. Now the flights would be monikered in a mystical and convoluted way that only the closest of Shuttle observers could follow. STS-10, for example became "STS-41B" with the "4" signifying the fiscal year in which the mission was scheduled, the "1" indicating that the launch was to take place at KSC as opposed to Vandenberg, where future Air Force launches were supposed to happen. The "B" indicated this was the second launch in the fiscal year. Thus, an STS-13 was completely avoided and the public at large was totally confused as to how many Shuttles NASA had actually flown. To NASA management it must have sounded quite clever, but the new numbering system immediately became hopelessly tangled. As payloads developed pre-launch issues and delays, and as vehicle issues caused schedules to slip, the numbering system got jumbled.

The first shuttle flight of fiscal year 1984, which started in October of 1983, was already in the books as STS-9 when it should have been STS-41A. Thus, the first flight in the calendar year of 1984 was STS-41B and it was followed by 41C and 41D. Mission 41F was eventually cancelled and no one knew what the hell happened to 41E, as the final flight of fiscal year 1984 became STS-41G launched on October 5, 1984. There would be one last mission launched in the calendar year of 1984, when STS-51A lifted off on November 8. In my world, only the editors of the Avion's Space Tech pages really knew which flights were which and why. I had too much aviation and flying information to stuff into my own brain to leave any room for NASA Headquarters and their latest mission designation scheme. So each Shuttle launch was simply the latest Shuttle launch to me, as it was with most of America.

STS-61A:
MORE HISTORY THAN I EXPECTED

For the most part I knew when the launches would take place and what the missions were all about because the Space Tech guys in the Avion office kept us all informed. On launch days I would either ride my bicycle to the bank of the Halifax River and watch the launch from Daytona, or simply find a good spot on Embry-Riddle's campus from which to watch the launches. Each time a new mission was scheduled, the Avion would get press credentials for two people. Normally the Space Tech editor would go and take some regular staff member along, but since I was only the cartoonist, I figured it was hard to justify me being that second person. After all, such a privilege was reserved for "normal" staff members – a designation that can never fit a cartoonist. Missions 51C, D, B, G, F, and I went by. Finally, as mission 51J was preparing to launch, I asked the Space Tech editor, Jim Banke, if I might have a turn to cover a mission. He happily agreed that I could go with him and help cover mission 61A in late October of 1985. Of course, even though I had witnessed 16 Shuttle launches with my own eyes, going to the press site was a major thrill for someone who grew up with spaceflight. I was looking forward to the adventure. What I would experience there, however, would go far beyond anything that I had ever imagined.

I was heavily steeped in college activities as the launch date approached. As chief pilot for the university's Precision Flight Team I had kept quite busy preparing the team for the regional flight meet and on top of that I was taking a full load of classes. In fact as Jim drove us down to KSC, I had my nose in a text book all the way there as I studied for an upcoming turbine engines exam. Of course as we rolled onto the space center I simply had to put down the text book and let that 15-year-old space-buff kid come out in me once again. Jim had covered nearly every launch over the past couple of years, and so he not only knew his way around the space center, he was known by nearly everyone there.

We had received our "News Media" badges ahead of time by mail and I pinned mine proudly to my shirt. As far as "credentials" at the space center can be considered, the badges for those early Shuttle launches were far below ordinary when compared to later badges. They consisted of a three-and-one-half-inch by two-and-one-quarter-inch piece of fluorescent-colored card stock with the triangular Space Shuttle logo in the upper right hand corner and the mission number in the left corner, with "News Media" printed below. At the bottom was a space for your name and the media outlet that you represented. The vehicle pass was simply a larger version of the badge. The color of the badges alternated with different missions. Our mission color was green. It was a simple system for a much simpler era.

(See Image 18, page 79.) Arriving at the press site on launch day, October 30, 1985, I was in awe. There were all of the buildings for the major networks. Out on the grass-covered field was the famous countdown clock and the bleachers were peppered with press from everywhere.

Jim led me around showing me everything, but I felt as if my eyes were not big enough to take it all in. It was like space-buff paradise. Jim knew who was who and where to stop first. That was the place he called "the goodie trailer." It was actually called the "Joint Industry Press Center," or JIPC, which everyone pronounced "gypsy." It somehow seemed appropriate as this was where all of the contractors let go with all of the free stuff for the media and VIPs. There were photos, booklets, buttons, key chains, bag-tags, pens, visors, mugs – you name it. It was all there for the taking! Now my hands seemed to be not big enough as I nabbed everything I could. More than three decades later, all I have remaining from that moment is a "D-1" mission pin. Oddly, to this day, there seems to be an unwritten rule at the press site that says, "don't talk about the freebies." As if throngs of spaceflight barbarians are going to come storming the press site demanding mission pins and contractor pens if they find out that those things are given away at the press site.

After we had been at the press site for about 45 minutes, Jim let me in on a little secret he had been keeping. As the current president of the school's student chapter of the L5 Aerospace Society, he had been asked to help escort a certain VIP among the news media.

"How'd you like to go meet Hermann Oberth?" he asked me.

At first I did not know who he was talking about, because from the time I was in the sixth grade I had been badly mispronouncing Professor Oberth's name whenever I read it. To me, the totally unsophisticated kid from the industrial Midwest, Wernher von Braun's mentor was a guy named "Here-man Ahbreath," so I did not recognize the name when it was properly pronounced. When Jim said this guy was von Braun's mentor, I immediately recognized my mistake and enthusiastically agreed to go and meet the man. Since STS-61A was lofting a German-sponsored space lab, Professor Oberth was there to see the launch. We soon found our way to the special area from where he would watch the launch and I got to meet and greet one of the fathers of modern spaceflight. Better yet was the fact that Professor Oberth was giving out autographed copies of his personal vision for the future in space. It was a one-page, typed document that was handed out by the assistant to the 91-year-old rocketry pioneer. Years later, one particular passage from that document would ring very true. It said;

"It is this generation of mankind who has the choice of which direction it will go; outward in peaceful exploration of boundless ends of space, or perish in stagnation of mistrust, despair and wasted energies."

(See Image 19, page 80.) Following our encounter with Professor Oberth, Jim got wind of another soon-to-be historic figure who had just arrived at the press site. It was the recently selected "teacher in space" Christa McAuliffe. We rushed over to the area where she could be found and waded through the crowd of reporters. Both Christa and her back-up, Barbara Morgan, were there together answering questions from the media. They made sure to actually "meet" everyone and the instant that you met Christa you knew exactly why she had been selected. She bubbled with personality and made you feel as if she had always known you and just happened to run into you at the local grocery store. You walked away feeling as if you had just said hello to a friend.

Having a teacher in space was a concept that had come out of the Regan administration and had gained almost universal favor in the public. Those of us who followed spaceflight pretty much figured, "What the heck. Why not?" After all, NASA had already tacked a senator and a congressman onto Shuttle crews plus one Saudi Prince, who did little more than look out the windows at one of his nation's satellites being deployed. So why not have a teacher flying aboard a Shuttle? It seemed logical to me and had the potential to be very good for awareness of spaceflight in general.

By the time we had finished talking to the two teachers in space, the countdown was coming out of the T-9 minute hold. The teachers, flanked by a group of us in the media, walked out to the grass field to stand and watch the launch. Jim stood fairly close to the teachers, but I broke formation and "skyed off" on my own. Jim had suggested that I go down and stand by the famous countdown clock. That way I would surely end up in photos of the launch. Instead I just went "fly-on-the-wall" and stood off on my own out of camera view. I figured that this would be my only chance to ever see a Shuttle launch from the press site and I wanted to try and take it all in.

(See Image 20, page 80.)Located just three-and-a-half miles from Pad 39A, the press site was as close as you could get to a Shuttle launch without being a NASA employee or having a death wish. Bunker number 7, where I had watched the STS-2 launch, was two miles farther away from the pads than the press site and I had high hopes that the shorter distance would make a difference -- and it sure did! The sound from the vehicle got to you much sooner and came in the form of repeated shockwaves. Even the ever-deadpan David Brinkley commented that at the press site the noise from the Saturn V made the change in your pockets jingle. The Shuttle was not much different.

Following the launch the press routine was far different than that of the launch-watcher on the NASA causeway. Instead of heading home in a traffic jam, we had to stick around for the post-launch press conference. Jim, in order to ensure that I was fully indoctrinated, made it clear that I was expected to ask a good question during the presser. It was required as a part of my obligation for representing the Avion at a Shuttle launch. I had to ask a question. So now I had to think up a good question.

We all gathered in the small auditorium where we would come face-to-face with the guys who had just launched the most complex vehicle ever conceived, and I had to ask a question; me, the guy who could had been mispronouncing Hermann Oberth's name since the sixth grade. Hell, I had been studying my butt off for a turbines test all week. I did not know squat about the Shuttle compared to the hardcore space reporters like Jim. Still, I went in and sat down and tried to come up with a question.

I had seen this same meeting room scene countless times on TV and the evening news. There was the elongated desk at the front with the microphones and chairs for the NASA guys. In the front was the huge "NASA worm" logo that on TV looked as if it had been carved out of stone with its letters painted red. When I looked closely, I saw that the damned thing was actually made of Styrofoam and the red letters were just red poster board that had been glued onto the face of the foam backing!

For a moment I considered that my question should be, "Why don't you get a real logo and get rid of the cheap foam thing?"

Then I could go up to the worm logo, rip off one of the letters and snap it in half in front of the TV cameras while exclaiming, "Look America! It's Styrofoam!"

Of course Jim would have killed me because I was supposed to be a space reporter today and not an editorial cartoonist.

Frankly, as of this writing, I do not recall what my question actually was, but it was technical, yet totally benign and the NASA official simply replied with a two or three word answer and they went on to someone else. I glanced over at Jim and he was not disapproving or embarrassed, so I guess I fulfilled my obligation. Still, I went away thinking I should have done the sign thing. That would have certainly made the news reports that evening. Well, it would have either been the image of me ripping up the NASA worm or Jim strangling me for doing it.

STS-61A:
"…TOO NUMEROUS TO MENTION"

When you are flying into busy airspace under visual conditions, air traffic control will sometimes simply advise you that your opposing traffic consists of multiple targets, "too numerous to mention." So it was that STS-61A went on with its mission, and the D-1, or Deutschland-1, space laboratory functioned flawlessly with 75 experiments – too numerous to mention here. The crew of CDR Hank Hartsfield; PLT Steve Nagel; NASA mission specialists Bonnie Dunbar, James Buchli and Guy Bluford; Ernst Messerschmid and Reinhard Furrer, both of West Germany; and Wubbo Ockels of ESA flew aboard the CHALLENGER for seven days, 44 minutes, and 51 seconds before landing safely on runway 15 at Edwards. After 112 orbits, this was the CHALLENGER's final mission in space and none of us knew it at the time.

On November 11, 1985, I was walking through the parking lot at Embry-Riddle on my way to the Avion office when I heard an unusual jet noise overhead. Looking up and scanning the bright Florida sky above me I spotted the 747 Shuttle Carrier Aircraft flying over on the Victor 3 airway headed back to KSC with the CHALLENGER on its back. Standing there I watched it as long as I could, totally unaware that I was witnessing a historic moment; the CHALLENGER's final return to KSC. In retrospect, I had gone to the launch of STS-61A simply because it was my turn. Yet I had met the father of modern rocketry face-to-face, I had met the "Teacher in Space" for whom we would all soon mourn, and I had witnessed the final return of the CHALLENGER.

It was a series of points in history, some of which were inspiring and others tragic. That, however, is a lesson that you learn when you become a historian; the events of history are more often tragic than inspiring. If one is to be a witness to history, you have to be willing to accept that fact. When it came to STS-61A, I had witnessed as an adult far more space history first-hand than I had expected, or ever dreamed of while growing up with spaceflight as a kid in Michigan.

STS-51L
THE 15-YEAR-OLD SPACE-BUFF DISSOLVES

When the 1986 spring trimester started at Embry-Riddle, I began a torrid love affair with a new sexy lady on campus. She was the Cessna T-303 Crusader. This sleek, shark-tailed aircraft was the hottest bird to ever sit on the flight line at ERAU, and for me it was love at first sight. She had trailing mains, counter-rotating three-bladed props, turbo-charged engines and cruised at flight-levels if you asked her to. I had just entered into the advanced flight courses and for the remainder of my time at ERAU this cabin-class twin was mine to fly.

(See Image 21, page 81.) During Skyfest '86 I was selected to be one of the pilots who would stay with her on static display. The night before the airshow I was lovingly polishing the T-303's chrome spinners when one of the university's instructor pilots came by and asked if I was "… gonna take that thing home and sleep with it?"

"Why not," I replied without missing a beat, "it treats me better than any woman ever has."

Originally, the university intended to order just two of these aircraft, but when the director of flight operations, while standing with both the new university president, General Ken Tallman, and some guy who was the Cessna's vice-president of sales, made the mistake of asking me how many I thought we needed, I told him flatly that we needed at least four. That was because once the pilots saw this baby they would all be standing in line to fly it.

He squirmed and said "We're only getting two,"

I insisted it would eventually have to be at least four. I saw General Tallman smile widely with a happy commanding officer's twinkle in his eye. Meanwhile I thought the guy from Cessna was going to wet his pants. We started with three Crusaders, but by the time I graduated there were four of those shark-tails on the line.

Although I had been able to watch the final Shuttle launch of 1985, STS-61B, a night launch, from the NASA causeway, the T-303 had all of my attention by the time that the first Shuttle mission of 1986, STS-61C, took place. I hardly noticed the mission because I was too busy punching my own holes in the Florida sky.

STS-51L was scheduled to launch on January 22, 1986, and it was being presented as something really special. It would carry aloft the "Teacher in Space," Christa McAuliffe. For weeks prior to the mission the teacher aspect of the flight was publicized to the point where all of the other objectives of the flight were completely muted by the news media. It is a good bet that nearly every school in the United States, as well as many others around the world were focused on the launch. Their students were about to learn some hard lessons that those of us in aviation already knew too well.

Launch day was pushed back several times for assorted reasons. First it was changed from January 22 to the 23rd and then the 24th because of conflicts with the long-delayed STS-61C. Next the date was changed to the 25th due to bad weather at the Dakar transoceanic abort site. When it was seen that Dakar's weather was not going to improve anytime soon, Casablanca was selected as the alternate, but since that runway was not equipped with the lighting needed for a night Shuttle landing, the launch time was changed from late afternoon to mid-morning. Other "processing" problems led to the launch date then being set for January 27 at 9:37 am. The launch was again rescheduled after a stubborn bolt prevented closing of the hatch and during that delay the cross winds at the Shuttle landing facility at KSC went out of limits causing an additional 24-hour delay. At length, the launch was set for 9:38 am, January 28, yet was again delayed by two hours due to a hardware interface module failing during LH2 tanking. Now, 11:38 would be the moment when the SRBs on STS-51L ignited and liftoff took place.

I was on my way back from the flightline that morning and headed toward a math class. While I was in the air we had been advised by Air Traffic Control as to the Shuttle's launch time, which was about 15 minutes after we got on the ground. Our own Flight Operations also made sure that everyone coming and going knew how the launch was progressing. I left the flight ops. building and after walking about three-quarters of the way across campus, I looked at my watch and stopped to watch the Shuttle rise above the horizon. It was a bitter cold morning, but the visibility was unlimited and the Shuttle was easily seen boosting toward space. Suddenly, I saw the External Tank explode. Then the SRBs could be seen continuing to fly without guidance. They slowly weaved across each other- it was very clear that something went real wrong.

My immediate thought was "RTLS Abort!"

RTLS was an acronym which stood for "Return To Launch Site," and was supposed to be the capability for the orbiter to simply glide back to the runway at KSC or even to ditch in the ocean nearby. Instantly I forgot math class and ran to the University Center (UC) where the nearest TV was located. I kept telling myself this was an RTLS abort. Very few of us, including big-time space-buffs like me, knew of the fact that RTLS could not be done during the burn of the solids. It was a dark little fact that NASA simply did not talk about and many people who actually worked with the Shuttle were unaware of as each launch took place. I got to the UC and the crowd around the TV was so big and there was so much talking that you could not hear a thing, so I sprinted up stairs to the Avion newspaper office where we had a small TV going. The three major broadcast networks, CBS, NBC and ABC were not covering the launch live, but local Florida news coverage was on the air. Although CNN's John Zarella – then just a rookie space reporter – was at KSC, CNN simply picked up the NASA feed at about T-3 minutes and allowed their anchor, Tom Mintier, to narrate the remaining countdown from Atlanta. No sooner had I stepped into the Avion office than I heard NASA PAO say the simple words "...we have no downlink."

That said it all to me.

That told me instantly that the vehicle was simply gone. No downlink meant that the devices that transmitted from the orbiter had been destroyed, and so had the orbiter.

At that moment the 15-year-old kid who sat in front of the TV with models of spacecraft and grew up with spaceflight seemed to dissolve away and what was left standing there was the adult professional aviator.

When one starts out to be a professional aviator you must learn some very fundamental lessons about that business; essentially they are the facts of life in aviation. The first of those statutes is what I have always called "the 50/50 rule." That rule is the simple fact that anytime you take the human animal and accelerate it to more than 50 knots or elevate it to more than 50 feet above the ground, or both, it can be killed. It does not matter how you dress it, how you strap it in, or how glorious the vehicle is, the rule still stands. The next rule is that aviation, in any form, is completely and terribly unforgiving of complacency, over-confidence or corner-cutting. The third rule is that all aviation accidents can eventually be traced back to management. The final rule is that management rarely, if ever, puts themselves in a position to be physically affected by these rules. As I stood there watching the TV images of the pieces of the CHALLENGER raining down I quietly said, "They're gonna find that this is management's fault."

STS-51L:
A BUTTERFLY TRYING TO RIDE A BULLET

In the days that followed the CHALLENGER's loss I wrote an editorial in the Avion that clearly stated my opinion that the accident's root cause would be traced to management. My friend and the paper's Space Tech editor, Jim Banke, who was a management major at the university and was at KSC on that awful day, wrote an impassioned rebuttal that focused on the technical side of the problem. In the months that followed, a series of investigations discovered that indeed the accident had its root cause in mismanagement. The SRBs were flown outside of their tested temperature envelope and the engineers who balked at the improper operation were told to, "Take off your engineer's hat and put on your management hat," in order to allow the launch to proceed. To make matters worse, the flight crew was never informed that this flight envelope excursion was taking place or even that it was suspected. When you remove the pilots from the Go/No-Go decision making of a flight, people will die. It is that simple. The pilots must always serve as the final trigger; the circuit breaker for the Go/No-Go decision making. And they must be provided with all of the information needed to make that decision.

Additionally, the "O" ring design of the SRBs was "a weak design" and several "burn-throughs" had been experienced on past missions, but schedule pressure kept management flying them without standing down in order to fix the design.

When the SRBs on mission STS-51L ignited, the CHALLENGER was doomed. Just 0.678 seconds into the flight photographs showed a puff of dark gray smoke coming from the aft field joint on the right hand SRB; the frozen rubber O-ring on the joint had been breached. Just over 59 seconds later the ultra hot gasses in the SRB had eroded through the joint and the resulting plume of flame was torching the ET, as well as the aft connecting fixtures for the right SRB. At a bit over 73 seconds into the flight the right SRB came loose at the base of the ET. Its nose rotated into the top of the ET, bursting the tank. That resulted in a "rapid burning" conflagration as thousands of tons of liquid oxygen and liquid hydrogen ignited and exploded. The orbiter was cast crossways into the supersonic slipstream at 1.92 Mach and the dynamic forces simply shredded the vehicle like a butterfly trying to ride a bullet. Although a few pieces remained intact, such as the three main engines, one wing and the crew cabin, the CHALLENGER was simply gone in an instant. Those large pieces continued upward to as high as 65,000 feet before beginning the long fall back into the ocean.

When the CHALLENGER was ripped apart by dynamic forces that only come in the worst nightmares of aerodynamics, and Christa McAuliffe lost her life as a result. I was angry, very angry. I was angry at the fact that this innocent person, who was not in the aviation profession, had done what most of our passengers do. She had placed her life, her trust, in those of us who were in the aviation profession, and our aviation profession had let her down. Those of us who dedicated our lives to flight know full well the risks, but those who we carry aboard our flying machines normally do not, so they trust us. I felt as if I had let her down myself, because I was a part of the aviation industry.

Investigations into the loss of STS-51L showed that both the "Level I" managers at NASA, as well as those at Thiokol, who made the SRBs, had known about the defects in the SRB field joints, yet kept flying them without standing down and fixing the problem. It also showed a correlation between the O-ring failures and low temperatures. Management in both institutions considered the O-ring erosions and blow-bys to be "an unavoidable and acceptable risk." But none of those managers had to ride on those same SRBs.

Wreckage from STS-51L came ashore as far north as Ormond Beach, Florida over the weeks following the loss. In fact some objects washed up within walking distance of the house where I was living.

STS-51L:
ONCE WAS ENOUGH FOR A LIFETIME

Later that summer I was back up in Michigan, working a summer job at Tri-City Airport, when I happened to meet CNN's science/space anchorman Tom Mintier in the lounge at the executive terminal. He was there to cover would-be presidential candidate Pat Robertson, who was arriving and being greeted by a throng of… exactly nobody. We started chatting about STS-51L and soon everyone nearby was listening. I told him my story and he talked about being live on the air at that moment.

"There's a few million people listening," he said glumly, "what do ya' say? There's just nothing you can say, the camera tells it all. There is simply nothing you can say."

Even six months after the accident you could see that both of us were still a bit lost by the event.

There would not be another Shuttle launched until September 29, 1988, when DISCOVERY would return the program to operational status as STS-26. The insanity of the flight monikers that no one could figure out was gone and so was the pressure of the schedule that had rolled over mission safety and crushed it like a rock under the crawler transporter. Most importantly was the fact that also gone was the notion that the Space Shuttle could be operated like an airliner under airline conditions.

Back during the launch of STS-1, ABC News' spaceflight

anchorman Jules Bergman stated, "NASA's made a big thing out of the Shuttle operating under airline type conditions. First they were talking about 560 flights in the next decade, now (those) have been scaled down to 460 flights, almost one flight a week and I think that is going to be impossible to support." Thumbing toward Pad 39A where STS-1 had just been scrubbed, he added that while it was reusable, "… that isn't a 747 and I don't think it ever will be."

Bergman had made similar statements way back on August 12, 1977, when the orbiter ENTERPRISE did its first free-flight; he was indeed correct.

By the time that the Space Transportation System was returning to flight, I had graduated from college and entered into the ranks of professional aviators actually earning a buck while allowing management their shots at killing me too. To this day I never watch when footage of the "CHALLENGER Disaster" is played on TV in documentaries. I simply turn my head, because I have seen it once, in person, with my own eyes. Once was enough for a lifetime.

STS-110:
84 MISSIONS JUST SLIPPED BY

Although there was a great deal of attention paid to STS-26, which was the "Return To Flight" mission following the CHALLENGER's loss, that all faded away rather quickly as soon as the Shuttles were again successfully flying. NASA finally got its wish that the missions of the Shuttle would one day become "almost routine." Those of us who grew up watching Mercury, Gemini, Apollo and Skylab on our parent's TV set found ourselves in adulthood as the Shuttle pressed on in that "almost routine" form of spaceflight. Thus, grown up concerns and careers tend to take one away from being a full-time space-buff. Of course it doesn't help when launches are only seen on the evening news. Sure CNN carried them live, starting their coverage within the last minute of the countdown and picking up the landings on short final approach. The media was convinced that there was little or no interest in the Shuttle among regular people. Apparently, the people who still flocked to KSC and parked a dozen cars deep on the NASA causeway to witness a launch did not count as "regular" people to the news executives.

Personally, I had tucked that 15-year-old space-buff, who had long been my alter ego, safely into storage as I chased after an aviation career. From survey pilot, to flight instructor, to airline pilot, to corporate pilot, I was usually far too busy getting my own butt off the ground to dedicate a lot of time to spaceflight. Additionally, I had started a second career as an author and research historian in the area of Great Lakes shipwrecks and found myself spending a lot of time poking around in the 1800s. Certainly, when I was on a layover in some hotel, I would turn the TV to the NASA channel and watch whatever was there. On occasion a Shuttle would be up and I would just let it all play there in the hotel room. One time as I was flying from Hibbing, Minnesota to Minneapolis in the hours before dawn, we were alerted that the Shuttle could be seen coming overhead. Looking up through the cockpit windows we saw it as a bright star moving rapidly to the east in the morning sky. Yet, one day I looked around, and after one fight school, three airlines and one corporate operation, it struck me that 84 Shuttle missions had simply slipped by me since I had witnessed the loss of the CHALLENGER on STS-51L.

It was the eighth day of April, 2002, and my wife and I were driving from Jacksonville, Florida to Orlando in order to attend an air show. On the way south the news came on the car radio that STS-110 was counting down for a 4:39 pm launch. Heck, that was pretty much on our way and so I suggested that we may want to stop and see it. That was when my wife of 14 years shocked me by saying that she had never seen a Shuttle launch from the Space Coast! Considering that she was, for the most part, raised in Jacksonville, and had attended Embry-Riddle in Daytona Beach with me and was even an editor-in-chief of the Avion newspaper, I simply had always thought that she had been down to KSC for Shuttle launches. But, nope, I was completely incorrect; she had never witnessed a Shuttle launch up close. In a heartbeat the decision was made. We were going to KSC to see STS-110, the 109th Space Shuttle launch.

Arriving at KSC we found that the Visitor Complex was closed and being used for VIPs and NASA guests with special passes. However, since wide-spread interest in the Space Shuttle was at an ebb tide at the time of STS-110, the nearby U.S. Astronaut Hall of Fame was wide open. Thus, at the direction of the NASA security man who was handling the traffic, we turned back and stopped there. I had never been to that site and found it to be terrific. It was also a good place from which to watch a Shuttle launch, primarily because it had restrooms. We found a good spot to watch the launch and I was able to witness the thrill that my wife got from seeing, and feeling, her first Shuttle launch up-close.

(See Image 23, page 82.) As we were driving away from KSC after the launch, she suggested that, aside from my Great Lakes authoring, I should consider doing some spaceflight writing. With that in mind I later started a spaceflight library in my home office and began to collect and research the subject. I had a lot to catch up on and a lot to re-learn, but I had friends who worked in the business of spaceflight, and that helped a great deal. Of course now that I was a professional author, spaceflight could not be a hobby- it had to become a book… or perhaps six.

STS-107:
NASA CAME FULL CIRCLE

I started to keep a closer track on the Shuttle than I had in years past, and that was no easy task. To a great degree, news coverage of the Shuttle was almost nonexistent by 2002. After all, Shuttle launches were averaging about one every two months in the late 1990s, so news outlets like CNN were only showing the liftoff and the landing roll – if they had time, of course. The first month of 2003, however, would change all of that.

NASA had come full circle from the schedule crush days of the CHALLENGER, where burn-throughs of SRB joints were considered an unavoidable and acceptable risk, to the launch of STS-107, where frozen foam shedding from the ET was considered to be the same. When launch video showed a large "briefcase sized" piece of foam shedding from the ET and striking COLUMBIA's left wing on the critical leading edge, some engineers and a few NASA managers had made requests for Department of Defense assets to be used to get more information about possible damage to the orbiter. That request also reached higher NASA managers at the Johnson Space Center and the word came down that "...nobody had a requirement for such information," and the request was ordered to be withdrawn.

To this day there is a debate about whether or not

the crew could have been saved had the discovery of a large hole in leading edge of the orbiter's left wing been confirmed. The debate is pointless, however. See my rules for aviation from the 51L chapter, rules that sadly were once again proven true.

Upon investigation of the accident it was concluded that the large chunk of foam which had broken off of the STS-107 ET and struck the left wing of the orbiter was the primary cause of the loss of the vehicle. The leading edge of the Shuttle's wing was made up of panels of Re-inforced Carbon-Carbon (RCC) which is highly resistant to heating and was thought to be stronger than steel. John Young later said that the astronauts had been told that you could beat on the RCC with a baseball bat and not hurt it. So, everyone worried about the fragile tiles, but never worried about the RCC. When that foam struck the RCC on COLUMBIA, however, it made a large hole that no one detected. Upon reentry the super-heated plasma that surrounded the vehicle had leaked into the hole and burned through the airframe like a blowtorch. Later, engineers at the Southwest Research Institute used a section of leading edge from the Shuttle ENTERPRISE and fired a 1.7 pound piece of ET foam at it in a manner similar that the way COLUMBIA was struck. To the amazement of everyone the foam left a hole the size of a pizza box.

(See Image 22, page 81.) Oddly, as STS-107 was happily orbiting around the Earth, my good friend Jim Banke sent me an e-mail asking why I had not yet done a cartoon strip spoofing the mission. I answered him, not like a cartoonist, or a fellow space-buff, but like the pilot that I am.

"I never do cartoons about on-going Shuttle flights," I said, "because I don't want one hanging out there when the next CHALLENGER happens."

Jim later told me those words haunted him as he sat in his Space.com news office, ready to publish a landing story, while listening for the sonic booms that would herald CO-LUMBIA's return to KSC, booms that never came.

Instead, COLUMBIA's breached heatshield led to its break up into thousands of pieces that fell across several states. Another seven astronauts were gone.

I had accidently slept through the loss of COLUMBIA that awful morning, but that accident awakened everyone. For the first time since STS-5, I think that the news media and the general public finally came to the realization that spaceflight, even in the Shuttle, is simply inherently danger-ous; and they accepted that fact. The politicians, however, could not accept that fact. The most disappointing among them was President George W. Bush, who mandated the retirement of the Shuttle, proposed a replacement for it and then turned around and ordered his Office of Management and Budget to underfund that same program. That spelled the end for the Space Transportation System and perhaps the end for all of NASA's human spaceflight launched from US soil for many years. Those of us who grew up with spaceflight would have to get all that we could out of what remained of the Space Shuttle missions.

Some spaceflight advocates found the Internet to be the best way around the old fashioned news media. Web outlets such as NASAspaceflight.com and Spaceflightnow.com began to grow rapidly and expand to fill the role so long ago vacated by the old TV news media. NASAspaceflight.com offered a wide range of forums, as well as a "Level Two," or "L2," area where a reader could sit at their keyboard and actually discuss subjects in-depth with actual astronauts and NASA engineers and managers as well as non-NASA rocket engineers. As of this writing it is the place to be to read and learn from the real experts. Meanwhile, Spaceflightnow.com took on the job of covering Shuttle launches live with broadcast video from the KSC press site. Hosted by Miles O'Brien, David Waters, and later Astronaut Leroy Chiao, and featuring countless guests, these "broadcasts" ran as long as six hours. So, as the Space Shuttle program pointlessly wound down, there were at least a lot of places where you could go to watch it do so.

STS-125
VIP... ME? NAAAAA.

It was the afternoon of May 11, 2009, and I found myself on the way to KSC to do something that I could never have imagined, not even in my wildest space-buff fantasies as a kid. That blistering hot Florida afternoon saw me driving down from Jacksonville to KSC in order to pick up credentials that would allow myself, my wife, my two little daughters and my father-in-law to all attend the launch of STS-125 officially as "VIP-NASA Launch Guests."

This entire event was simply blowing my mind. Me? A VIP? a "Very Important Person"? Hell, I never thought of myself as qualifying for the "I" part of that acronym let along the "V" part. Frankly, I often wonder if I qualify for the "P" part. After all, I am just a space-buff from the wrong side of Saginaw, Michigan. I still think of myself as the weird kid on the block who shot rockets from his backyard and scared the crap out of the neighbors. Now here I was, more than three decades later, tooling into the VIP parking area at the KSC Visitor Complex and leading my family into the "will-call" area to pick up our credentials for the next day's Shuttle launch. Life is almost as curious as the circumstances that led us all there that day.

My elevation from slob space-buff who watches Shuttle launches on NASA TV to VIP NASA Launch Guest came in a fairly strange series of events that I also could not have hidden and stored away in the strangest corner of my twisted space-buff brain. It all sort of began four-and-one-half-years earlier at the legendary Mojave Airfield in the High Desert of California near Edwards Air Force Base. I was there with the Aero-News Network covering the private spaceflight competition known as the "X Prize." In fact I had an artifact that rode into space on the final flight aboard SpaceShipOne; a plush doll of my cartoon character Klyde Morris. Although most of the media was there for the first flight and then quickly departed back to civilization for a week, our crew remained at Mojave. When the second flight was over and SpaceShipOne had claimed the X Prize the media all gathered in a small auditorium for the post-event presser.

Once inside I noticed that seated in the front row was CNN's space and science anchorman Miles O'Brien. Over the last dozen or so years Miles had become the best spaceflight anchor on TV and by this time, as far as space-buffs were concerned, he had managed to rise to the level of a Jules Bergman or Frank McGee. Even Walter Cronkite had telephoned him, live on the air, during the CNN coverage of the COLUMBIA accident and told him that he was, "doing a great job" covering that event. Thus, I felt compelled to step over and tell him that I liked his work, not that my words would mean a whole lot, but what the heck. Miles was very polite and thanked me for the compliment. Then I saw him glance up at my Klyde Morris hat and then my press I.D.

Hey," he said with a wide smile, "I know you! I read your cartoon strip!"

I was quite astonished, although I had written a few cartoons lampooning Miles and depicting his office at CNN as being in a former broom closet, I never expected that he had read the darned things. We laughed a bit and I told him I would send him a print of the cartoons suitable for framing. We kept in brief contact over the next few years and when CNN decided it no longer needed a science and technology department, and then fired everyone in it, including Miles, I made sure to use my cartoon strip to take some hard shots in the network's direction. Apparently the thought was that covering reality TV stars and wayward political stars was more important than covering the actual stars in the sky. Their channel has been trash since that point.

In early 2009, Miles sent me a message saying that he was going to be the host of the Rotary National Award for Space Achievement (RNASA) Foundation Award Dinner again and he was looking for some spoof spaceflight video to open the show. The event was not going to take place until around the end of April, so there were a few months to work on the video and he assured me that we would coordinate on the project. Of course, Miles being Miles, he had a very full plate and soon completely forgot about the video. About a week before the event he contacted me in a near panic, but I assured him that I had enough stuff in the can already to give him what he needed. A couple of days later he dropped in at my home and I showed him the video that I had.

"It's all here," he said in relief, "you really saved my bacon."

We shot some additional video on the spot in order to get the production that Miles wanted, his bacon thus remaining intact.

While we were downloading my stuff to his laptop we started talking about the upcoming STS-125 launch that would take place in about two weeks. He asked if I was going down for it and I said that the whole family was going down because I wanted my two little daughters to at least be able to say that they had seen a Shuttle launch before the program ended. He asked where we were going to watch from. I said that we would probably try Jetty Park or some such thing.

Miles frowned a bit and asked, "What about the VIP site?"

I scoffed and half laughed saying that I could not possibly get into the VIP site because I was NOT a VIP. With that he whipped out his Blackberry and shot off a text message.

"We'll see about that," he quipped.

A moment later he got a reply back, then sent another message. When that reply came back, Miles glanced up and matter-of-fact said, "Okay, you're in." The next day I got a call from KSC Director Bob Cabana's office. After taking all of my information the arrangements were made; the space-buff slob from the wrong side of the river was elevated to VIP NASA Launch Guest!

STS-125:
THERE WAS NO DESIGNATED
AREA FOR SLOBS

STS-125 was to be the last servicing mission for the Hubble Space Telescope. The orbiter ATLANTIS was assigned to the mission, along with the crew of Commander Scott Altman; Pilot Gregory C. Johnson; and Mission Specialists Megan McArthur, Andrew Feustel, John Grunsfeld, Mike Massimino and Michael Good. NASA said that the crew was to do a series of five EVAs. They would install two new instruments and repair two others, plus replace gyroscopes and batteries, and add new thermal insulation panels to protect the Hubble. A new Wide Field Camera would allow Hubble to observe in ultraviolet and infrared spectrums, as well as visible light. Thus, it could peer deeper into the cosmic distance and search for the earliest star systems, and also study planets in our solar system. The telescope's new Cosmic Origins Spectrograph also would allow it to study the overall structure of the universe, including the star-driven chemical evolution that produces carbon and the other elements necessary for life. The crew of STS-125 had a huge and complex mission ahead.

Launch was scheduled for the civilized time of 2:01 in the afternoon, which was great for me because I had the entire family in tow. Awakened and fed we headed out early that morning, driving from Melbourne north to

KSC. Traffic was lighter than I had expected and we rolled slowly along toward the Visitor Complex. Along the way I told my wife that for the second time in my life I wished that I did not know about all of the countless things that could go wrong and cause a scrub of the launch. We had also planned a side trip to Disney World right after the launch, and so a scrub or delay could leave me witnessing the launch from Frontierland. My kids would be happy, but Daddy would be not-happy.

On launch day the parking area at the Visitor Complex was clearly divided into regular people parking and VIP parking. There was no designated area for slobs from the wrong side of town who are space-buffs, so we just wheeled into VIP with our window coral-colored placard in place.

We walked up to the guard gate, were checked off the list and went in through the VIP door. My two little girls, one being a toddler and the other a preschooler, were far more interested in the huge jungle-gym that was located in the Visitor Complex than they were in the rocket garden. We were clearly not alone, however, as a lot of folks were making their way toward the busses that were transporting people to the VIP site. Soon that kid who grew up with spaceflight came bubbling to the surface and I got antsy to find a seat on a bus. We gathered the kids and were politely guided to a waiting luxury bus. Once aboard it was very clear that the folks at KSC were as competent and professional at handling VIPs as they were at launching Shuttles. They had the whole affair down to a science. Each of us was issued a two and one quarter inch diameter white and red button to pin on. It had a black NASA meatball on the top, and Shuttle stack to the right and bold lettering that said "Launch Guest," and below was denoted, "Kennedy Space Center, Florida." Pinning mine to my shirt exactly as instructed, I was worried that the NASA folks would be collecting the buttons after the event, for "security reasons." Rapidly I fashioned a plan where my toddler would somehow lose hers and I would just happen to find it the next day in my pocket.

(See Image 24, page 82.) The VIP site in 2009 was a far different adventure than it had been back in 1981 when, by luck alone, I viewed the STS-2 launch from its location at "Bunker Number 7." On that occasion they had redirected the causeway's bus overflow to the VIP site and I just happened to be on one of those busses. Back then the VIP site was an earthen revetment that had once been a camera site and NASA had taken the time to install some aluminum bleachers to seat their guests. By the time of STS-125, nearly three decades later, the "Apollo Saturn V Center" was serving as the VIP site. The busses casually pulled in and dropped off the VIPs all wearing our white and red buttons. I guess the real VIPs back during STS-2 had some sort of buttons as well, but not being a VIP in any sense of the word, all I had that day was a squished peanut butter and strawberry jam sandwich and a thermos of hot tea, which I thought was quite appropriate.

A sprawling building, the Apollo Saturn V Center contains a horizontally displayed Saturn V launch vehicle as well as assorted other Apollo flight hardware that properly belongs in space rather than in a museum. The center opened its doors to the public in December of 1996. Contrary to what most would like to believe, the Saturn V on display in its namesake building is not all "flight hardware." The S-IC first stage is actually the S-IC-T stage that was extensively used in ground test firings. It was originally placed on display, along with the other launch vehicle components now in the museum, outdoors next to the VAB in 1976 as part of a bicentennial celebration. It remained outdoors in the harsh Florida sun until the Saturn V Center was opened twenty years later. During its restoration it was configured to appear like the sixth S-IC flight stage that boosted Apollo 11, but underneath, it is still the S-IC-T. On display as the second stage of the Saturn V is an actual piece of flight hardware, the S-II-14 stage. This flight stage would have boosted either the Apollo 18 mission or it would have been used as the back-up booster to place into orbit the back-up Skylab workshop. Since both of those missions were never flown, neither was the stage. It is important to consider, when looking at that S-II stage, that all five of its J-2 engines, although they look new, have actually been static fired for 373.2 seconds; just under three seconds short of full duration of 376 seconds. The S-IVB third stage in the display was also constructed as a flight stage, but was never test fired. Assembled in 1968, the stage did not have its J-2 engine installed until January 28, 1970. By then budgets and missions for Apollo were being cut and the future for all spaceflight hardware was growing bleak. Three years later the stage was flown to KSC and placed in long term storage, arriving on March 28, 1973, and going into mothballs on the fourth day of April. Still, the Saturn V display is beyond awesome and anytime I get to go and see it I make sure to do so simply so that I can stand and gaze at it.

Normally, the center itself provides plenty of room for folks to stroll around and look in wonder of what we, as Americans, were once able to do. Normally it is also a rather quiet place. At least you are able to hear announcements over the public address system. On a Shuttle launch day, however, the story was different as scores of VIPs jammed into the building. The din of conversation and crowd noise was so loud that it drowned out the speakers in the public address system. I found it was nearly impossible to hear the loop and monitor the countdown. To a space-buff, every word spoken by the launch controllers is important because each can point to a glitch that can result in a scrub. I found myself standing right under a speaker in order to get just bits and pieces of information. Finally I gave up and just decided to dedicate myself to helping my kids, my wife and my father-in-law enjoy the experience. Still, my father-in-law kept asking about the launch and I kept telling him that I could not hear a thing, "but if they're counting, they're goin.'"

My concern also turned to my little toddler. She was always terrified by two things: fire and loud noises. Now I was about to expose her to a flame that was nearly as bright as the sun and to the third loudest noise ever made by humans – the second loudest being a Saturn V launching and the first loudest being a Soviet N1 exploding. What kind of a father was I? Of course, being a true space-buff I simply reasoned that she could someday work it all out in therapy.

One huge advantage of being at the VIP site was that there are lots of real astronauts milling around. My oldest daughter, the preschooler, got to meet Astronaut Mike Foreman, who was kind enough to stop and stoop with her so that we could take several photos. He also listened to what she knew about spaceflight and was a great example to a little girl of what an astronaut should be. Five months later she and I would watch as Foreman did EVAs during STS-129. I pointed at the computer monitor and told her that was the guy she met at the Shuttle launch. She would look with a few moments of wonder and then go back to her mermaid toys.

As the count for STS-125 came out of the T -9 minute hold I started to gather the flock together in order to go outside for the launch. It was then that my wife suddenly decided that this was a good time to take the kids to the potty.

WHAT!? A potty visit with the kids takes at least 15 minutes! We are inside of nine minutes to launch – this was insane!

Still, there is no stopping a mommy when it comes to a potty break for the kids. Luckily, she managed to get them in and out with two minutes left in the count.

Scrambling outside we found the bleachers were filled. I told everyone to just stand were they were in the grass and look at the pad. "You cannot miss this thing." Once outside of the Apollo Saturn V Center's building, the loop could clearly be heard and everything sounded nominal. The count went down to liftoff without a hitch. All of my scrub fears were instantly erased and I watched my family wonder in awe at the majesty and glory of the Space Shuttle. My preschooler had been coached by me to shout "Go baby, GO!" but she simply stood there with her wide eyes riveted to the ascending Shuttle. I nudged her and I started shouting "GO!" She quickly followed although her little voice was nearly obliterated by the power of the Shuttle. Then I looked over toward my toddler expecting her to be in a tearful fright. Instead, she had her little head turned skyward in amazement and while pointing toward the Shuttle she kept saying, "Yook, yook!"

Shortly after MECO we were back on the bus and headed back to the Visitor Complex in complete comfort. As a space-buff I had watched a lot of NASA events on TV, as well as witnessing a few first-hand, and along the way to growing up with spaceflight I had also imagined a lot of things that I might do. Yet, this event was beyond anything I could have dreamed up. My wife was happy that everything had gone so well and that the folks at NASA had treated us so wonderfully. My father-in-law now had bragging rights with all of his friends in Jacksonville because if any of them had seen a Shuttle launch, they most likely had not done so from the VIP site. Most importantly, my two little daughters had been thrilled by the launch. That event remained at the top of their amazing things list, right up until the next day when we arrived at Walt Disney World.

For the record, STS-125 went on to accomplish a perfect mission. The Hubble Space Telescope was serviced and would collect amazing images for many years to come. After 12 days, 21 hours, and 37 minutes, the crew brought ATLANTIS back safely to Earth. By then I was back home watching the landing on NASA TV and highly satisfied by the fact that NASA actually let us keep all of our white and red "Launch Guest" buttons. The STS-125 launch was probably the only time that this space-buff from the wrong side of town would ever be elevated to the level of VIP by NASA and it was all thanks to my friend Miles O'Brien.

STS-130 & STS-131:
FROM MY STORM DECK TO
MY HOSPITAL BED

As the year 2010 began the Shuttle program was seriously winding down and I was able to be "credentialed" to cover launches from the KSC press site, but life, family and circumstances seemed to prevent my doing so. An additional roadblock to such activity was the post-COLUMBIA propensity for launches to be scrubbed. There was little sense in arranging for all of the home front matters, such as kids in school and pre-school and other work at my desk, then buying a plane ticket, getting a hotel and rental car just to go down for a scrub and a delay that could take days or even weeks. So, the best place from which to cover the launches appeared to be my desk at home.

Do not get me wrong. None of the Shuttle scrubs were NASA's "fault," they just seemed to simply be happenstance. NASA had shed the schedule burden and was now guided by a strong dose of common sense plus operating strictly by its own rules, to the letter. Additionally, annoying malfunctions seemed to just crop up and needed trouble shooting. STS-114, the "Return To Flight" mission following the COLUMBIA disaster, was delayed two weeks because Engine Cutoff (ECO) sensors in the ET acted up. Then at launch, foam shedding during STS-114's ascent caused a delay of just under a year before the next mission,

STS-121, could be launched on July 4, 2006. That mission's launch, however, was delayed by four days due to weather. STS-115, the next Shuttle to be launched, was delayed from August 27, 2006, to September 9, due to everything from Hurricane Ernesto to more faulty ECO sensors; the most annoying part of that taking place during the countdown on September 8 when the ECO sensor issue stopped the whole show during the T-9 minute hold. STS-116 was scrubbed during the countdown due to weather and delayed an extra day in order to allow a cold front to pass. It successfully launched on December 9, 2006. After a three-month delay due to hail damage to ATLANTIS, STS-117 launched as scheduled. STS-118 also launched as scheduled, as did STS-120 the next mission in line. STS-122, however, fell prey to the ECO sensor problems again and launch attempts in 2007 on both its December 6 and December 9 were scrubbed. Finally on February 7, 2008, STS-122 got into space. The following month, on March 11, STS-123 launched as scheduled and STS-124 also did an on-schedule departure on May 31. On November 14, STS-126 launched as scheduled for a Thanksgiving mission in space. STS-119, however, suffered a launch day scrub due to another issue that would annoy space-buffs around the world; a leak in a Ground Umbilical Carrier Plate (GUCP). The GUCP acronym can easily be pronounced either by hiccupping, or attempting to clear a popcorn husk from the back of your throat. Next up was STS-125 which flew as scheduled, but the next flight, STS-127, made up for it by scrubbing not once, not twice but five times; two for GUCP leaks and three for weather. Just over a month later STS-128 scrubbed twice: once for a LH2 fill valve issue and once for weather, yet finally got off the pad on August 28, 2009. So, although STS-129 launched on time, I considered the recent track record and decided to monitor the flights from the desk in my home office on the Chesapeake Bay rather than buy plane tickets and cover a scrub. The odds were on my side.

By 2010 and STS-130, coverage on CNN had gone down the toilet and the former "Big Three" networks of NBC, ABC and CBS were nowhere to be found as far as the space program was concerned. However, if you were a Hollywood star doing something disgusting, or a sports hero falling from grace, the networks were all over it.

FOX News tried hard to cover space events and it showed. Their Florida regional anchor Phil Keating had been busily working his way into the tight circle of KSC spaceflight reporters and uses a laid-back style that led me to lampoon him in my cartoon strip as being the journalist who wind-surfs into the space center, has his hair and makeup done by a dozen Hawaiian Tropic models in bikinis and then jet-skis home when he's done. He is surely one of the coolest reporters I have ever met. At one launch as he was standing in front of the camera and waiting to come out of commercial, I told him that my 70-year-old Mom was watching up in Michigan. He asked if I wanted him to, "do the ear-tug for her?" I said "Yeah!" and I quickly called Ma on the phone, telling her to watch. When he came back on he began reporting and casually reached up and tugged at his ear. Some 1,068 miles away my Mom squealed with delight; no one else really noticed. She thus became a lifelong Phil Keating fan.

Overall, however, the best coverage was on Spaceflight-Now.com and their live broadcasts with Miles O'Brien, David Waters and Leroy Chiao. I often stayed up all night watching every aspect of the mission on my computer by way of those broadcasts.

Liftoff was at 04:14:08 Eastern Time on February 8,

2010, for STS-130. It was the second attempt for this mission. The first try had been scrubbed the previous morning due to weather. I sat at my desk feeling somewhat satisfied that I had not invested in the trip down to cover the scrub, yet knowing that I was missing the spectacle of the later launch. Seeing the Shuttle rocket into orbit was always the experience of a lifetime, no matter how many times you had experienced it. I found myself, as always, wishing that I could see it first-hand. It was about then that the image of the Shuttle's ascent track was displayed on my computer. Flying on an inclination of 51.6 degrees it was traveling nearly up the east coast of the United States, and this was four o'clock in the morning. Maybe I could see it! Stepping out onto what we call our "storm deck," which faces due east over Chesapeake Bay from the third floor of our home, I saw that it was an amazingly clear night. Still, I pondered that the Shuttle could perhaps be below the trees.

With the mission's live audio playing in the background I listened to NASA's PAO announcements. Soon, higher above the horizon than I expected, came an amber tinted first magnitude star moving faster than any aircraft other than the Shuttle could. Yet, I had my doubts and so I calculated that there was only one way to know if that was indeed the Shuttle. If the fast moving light went out at MECO, it was the Shuttle. For about two minutes I watched the light and then it suddenly went out! A heartbeat later, Mission Control announced MECO! After three decades, I had gotten to witness a part of the Shuttle that I had never seen before with my own eyes: press to MECO and MECO itself.

Amazed, I went to my computer and logged onto NASAspaceflight.com's forum and asked if anyone else in my area had witnessed what I saw. Sure enough, two other space-buffs had seen ENDEAVOUR's MECO as well; one guy in the Washington D.C. area and another fellow in the New Jersey area. Later that morning, as my wife prepared to go to work, she asked about the launch, "How was it?" and "Was it worth stayin' up all night?" I said "Yes" and added that I had seen it with my own eyes and then gleefully described watching it press to MECO. She was unimpressed and just shook her head and told me to try and get some sleep. When you're married to a life-long space-buff, tolerance is a virtue.

Just two months after the launch of STS-130, I again witnessed another Shuttle launch from my desk. Again, the Shuttle launched in pre-dawn darkness. The date was April 5, 2010, but this time it could not be seen from my storm deck due to a heavy overcast of clouds. Yet, STS-131 would provide great comfort for me in a way that I had not imagined, not even in my wildest nightmares.

On the Friday following the launch I got up at my normal pre-dawn hour, went up to my office and began working. The EVAs that had been planned for STS-131 were all scheduled to take place in the middle of the night, so I simply elected to keep my daytime schedule and catch the EVAs on re-play. Sitting at my desk I began to feel an ache in the left side of my back. Thinking I had pulled a muscle or slept on it wrong I reached behind me and gave the area a rub.

WHOA! MISTAKE!

The pain quickly intensified to the point where it was something debilitating. I struggled downstairs and enlisted the help of my wife. An agonizing hour and a half later we were in the Emergency Room checking me in. The check-in nurse asked what my problem was, but when I told her it came out as "Grmphthdresmfunarrrggg." She slid a paper at me and told me to fill it out. I tried, but that also came out as, "Hugmsn shlungnatfraarrrrrggg." My wife took over and did the paperwork. The nurse then asked me to follow her to the examining room.

"Just drag me to the cemetery," I snarled.

Mercifully, my examining room wait was brief and when the doctor on-call came in he asked where the pain was located and what it felt like. I growled something about being shot in the side with a whaling harpoon.

Before long a second nurse came in with an I.V. rig and said, "Honey, I'm about to become your best friend."

As she let the drip on the Dilaudid flow, my agony simply melted away.

Later in the day they found that rather than a whaling harpoon, a fairly large kidney stone was the cause of my discomfort. It was also later determined that surgery would be required to remove the stone. That surgery could not be done until Monday, so I would have to spend three nights in the hospital.

Spending time in the hospital is to be avoided at all costs in my opinion. The days could be tolerated only because they had me hooked up to drugs that would make any experience seem happy. Nights were another matter. First of all they poke and prod you every couple of hours so you cannot sleep, and my night nurse was right out of a horror movie. I began to avoid going to sleep because I feared she may harvest my organs and sell them on the black market. Those nights would have been completely intolerable had it not been for the STS-131 mission.

As it turned out the local public access channel on the cable TV that came into my room switched from politicians bloviating about county politics and school board meetings to NASA TV at 11:00 pm. On two of my three nights in the hospital, I was able to lay there and watch non-stop EVA coverage from the ISS. Not only did that keep me occupied, but it also kept me awake and may have kept my organs from being harvested by the night nurse.

(See Image 25, page 83.) On April 20, the orbiter DISCOVERY rolled to a stop at KSC's Shuttle Landing Facility. That was the end of STS-131 and I was well over my kidney stone. Watching the orbiter roll out, I said a small "Thank You" to the mission for the comfort that it gave me those nights in that hospital bed and for, perhaps, saving me from that evil nurse. In retrospect I learned one huge lesson in life from that whole ordeal. If you really, really hate someone, do not wish death upon them. Wish them a kidney stone… it's worse.

STS- 135:
ALPHA-OMEGA

Originally the final Shuttle mission that would become STS-135 was not to be flown at all; it had been a "launch on need" rescue vehicle backing up the STS-134 mission and was originally scheduled as STS-335. Although in his pre-election 2008 paper on America's future in space, dated August 16 of that year, then candidate Barack Obama had promised to "…work to ensure there is adequate funding to support that additional flight (STS-135)…" Once elected he simply stood silent on the matter, other than the White House "hinting" that Obama may relax the Bush deadline of retiring the Shuttle in 2010. By simply "voting present," Obama's non-leadership would be allowing the Bush schedule to stand. Congress acted, however, and both houses approved funding for STS-135 in the early autumn of 2010. Obama grudgingly signed the authorization into law on October 11, yet left the fate of the mission up to the passing of the upcoming Federal Budget. That budget was finally passed in April of 2011, and STS-135 was officially a flying mission. I immediately contacted my editor at the Aero-News Network and told him that I wanted credentials to go and cover the launch, and he happily agreed.

When the July 8, 2011, launch date for STS-135, the final flight of the Space Shuttle, was announced I had the feeling I was screwed on covering the launch. After a quick look at my calendar, I was sure. I was screwed. Unfortunately, the family summer vacation road trip, that we had been planning for nearly a year was scheduled to depart on that same date. So, the final launch of the Shuttle would take place while I was in the family van headed up I-70. It was a pretty depressing thought, since I had been there for the very first Shuttle launch and I had been holding the hope of attending the final launch. Still, plans had been made, hotel reservations were in place and a family reunion was on the schedule. NASA's plans had simply conflicted with those of my family.

I did my best not to mope in the open. After all, this vacation had been my idea in the first place. The best that I could do was wish for a scrub that would last a few weeks. An issue involving the Main Fuel Valve on one of the Space Shuttle Main Engines (SSME) looked promising for a while, but it was easily corrected at the pad with no impact on the launch date. I came shuffling downstairs from my office and mentioned to my wife that the SSME problem was going to be cleared. After a quarter of a century together, she sensed what I was trying to hide.

"Ya' know," she suggested, "if we modified our travel plans just a little bit you could go down for that launch."

I replied with some doubt, but she insisted,

"You were there for the first one and it's only appropriate that you should be there for the last one. I mean, how many people can say that?"

There are lots of times when I know that I have married the right lady, and this was yet another one.

"Sort of an alpha-omega," I replied with a smile referring to the Greek letters symbolic for the first and the last.

"Exactly," she grinned.

In less than a half hour our vacation was slightly altered and I had my plane tickets booked.

STS-135:
IF ONLY THE POLITICIANS CAN
KEEP THEIR HANDS OFF OF IT

As the year 1981 began it had been five-and-one-half years since the last Americans had been launched from the Kennedy Space Center. The psyche of the American public had been shoved through the turmoil of the late 60s and then dragged through the "change" of the 70s. So, as STS-1 was prepared to fly from Pad 39A, the prospect of the United States starting a new and spectacular adventure in space quickly captured the imagination of a pride-parched American public. Over the previous half decade the news media, having cut new sharp teeth on Watergate, had done their best to highlight every fault and failure in the development of the Shuttle. Most of the public, however, had been too dazzled by disco balls to notice. By April of 1981 a real, flight-ready, fully-functional Space Shuttle sat waiting on the pad as if to spite its critics.

Camping out on the riverbank in Titusville prior to the launch, all of us who were there knew that we were going to witness history, one way or another. I knew that this launch would be the ultimate in "all-up testing." Such testing involved launching an entire, amazingly complex vehicle as a single working unit instead of launching and testing one component at a time. This time, however, unlike the Apollo Saturns, which were all-up tested unmanned, the

Shuttle would be tested with astronauts aboard. It was a pinnacle in flight test that will never again be attempted or reached. A full chapter in aviation history was going to be written right in front of us and that reality sunk in to a few of us more than it did to most folks who were watching. We were the ones who had quite literally grown up with spaceflight.

At Main Engine Start we saw the three SSMEs ignited and come up to full thrust with perfection. This was in spite of the media telling us about the numerous SSME failures and even a few explosions that had taken place in development, and the implication that this could very well happen on STS-1. Then the largest solid rocket boosters on Earth ignited in precise unison, again contrary to media implications of disaster. Raining fire, STS-1 gracefully arced into the morning sky with an earth-shaking roar that awakened the American spirit. On the river bank we screamed and shouted everything from "GO! BABY GO!" to the "WOOOO!" of rebel yells. At SRB sep an estimated near one million people spontaneously broke into applause. We looked at the smoke trail left by the SRBs with the feeling that this was the start of something new, something big; something to be proud of once again. Knowing spaceflight history like I did, I tempered that feeling with the thought of,

"If only we can keep the politicians' hands off of it."

Yet at that moment in time, it looked as if John Young had been correct when, after STS-1, he said that America was in space to stay. We were both wrong.

In a knee-jerk reaction to the loss of the COLUMBIA in 2003, President Bush directed that NASA must do three things. First, it must set a course and develop vehicles to return to the Moon and go on to Mars. Second, it must retire the Shuttle by 2010. Third, it must abandon the

International Space Station by 2015. This all was the president's "Vision for Space Exploration" and it sounded as if we were advancing into space in spite of the COLUMBIA accident.

Unknown to most of the public, Bush then directed his Office of Management and Budget to short-change NASA by an amount for nearly $3 billion a year; exactly the amount needed to accomplish his "Vision." This political three card monte game left a "gap" in NASA's manned spaceflight program as no new vehicles could be afforded before the Shuttle was mandated to be "retired." NASA's only option would be to rent seats on the Russian Soyuz vehicles until the "Vision" vehicles were ready. Bush's little game thus doomed the Shuttle and left open the door for an anti-NASA president to later gut the agency. Enter Barack Obama and the outright cancelation of the "Vision," its return to the Moon and the vehicles to replace the Shuttle. By allowing the Shuttle program to die on the Bush schedule, and by canceling its replacement, Obama could successfully neuter NASA's human spaceflight program and "change" the agency into little more than a federal think-tank. So, I knew that the mission of STS-135 would be the swansong of the Shuttle program and perhaps may become the end of NASA's human spaceflight program as well.

STS-135:
"BITTERSWEET?" WHERE'S THE SWEET?

When I arrived in Florida on the day prior to the launch, a tropical weather system was sweeping over the Space Coast and a steady rain was falling upon KSC. All of the hard-surfaced parking area at the press site was filled with news satellite trucks and support trailers, so parking was left to the grass lot, which was quickly turning into a mud pit. After a brief visit to the press building, I decided to head out before my rental car needed a tow truck in order to do so. That evening a group of people who haunted the NASAspaceflight.com web site all gathered in a reserved room at a Titusville seafood place for a pre-launch dinner. Prior to that moment we had all known each other strictly by "usernames," on the Internet and thus this was our one chance to meet face to face. The room was filled and we all had a great time in spite of the shadows hanging over the American manned space program.

Arriving at the KSC press site on launch morning was predicted to be "bittersweet," yet for me it was more bitter than sweet. It was 4:30 in the morning and I had planned my early arrival to beat the traffic. Although I was successful in that, I found myself parked in the third row of the over-flow and directly in front of a small gate leading through the press site fence. The predawn morning was devoid of stars as that same sub-tropical weather system from the previous day was still smothering the Space Coast. Although the press site was brightly lit, the chances of a launch were quite dim as the weather seemed ready to force a scrub.

Normally, the press room is haunted by two basic categories of reporters, what I like to describe as the "hardcores" and the "meatpuppets." The hardcores are the gang of spaceflight media who are there for almost everything: Shuttle, Falcon 9, Atlas, Delta, even Ares I-X. They are a bunch who can bring up a technical question, bounce it around each other for a few minutes and come up with the absolutely correct answer. Although you rarely, if ever, will see them on your TV, they know each other by name, face and reputation and I always feel lucky to occasionally sit among them. The meatpuppets, on the other hand, are the people assigned by their network to cover an event, about which they know almost nothing. Of course they do the same task all the time anyway, so what difference does it make this time? Whether covering a murder trial or an oil spill, it is all the same to them. They get handed a few notes, look into the camera or transcribe a press release and then they move on to the next story.

(See Image 26, page 83.) For those of you who grew up with spaceflight, but have not had the opportunity to work from the press site, a bit about being there to cover a launch might be helpful to know. It IS a major experience, at least for me. The press site itself is the same one that was used for Apollo, except now the press has their own building rather than sitting outside in bleachers. In order to qualify for press credentials you must be associated with an approved media outlet and there are a number of acid tests that your individual application must go through to get approved. The folks at NASA have the system down pat too, so there is no faking your way in by saying you are a reporter. They check REAL close on every application, every time. In my case I was with the Aero-News Network which, although internet-based, passes the muster easily.

After picking up my badge, I was allowed to enter the space center and go to the press site, in my own car, by myself. I have to tell you that although some in the hardcore space reporter gang may yawn at the experience, I always have cherished the opportunity. Every time I drive in, as soon as they clear me through the gate, I once again turn into a 15 year old space-nut. I just sit there wide-eyed and take it all in and giggle to myself. There is the VAB, and there are the crawlers. Turn right at the VAB on the same road that takes the astronaut van to LC-39 and a sense of total wonder comes over you. The press site is the last turn before the road goes out to the pads. You do not want to miss that turn because guys with machine guns and no sense of humor lay beyond. At the press site you see the same buildings where Cronkite, McGee, Chancellor and Bergman sat and reported launches with Saturn Vs over their shoulder. I swear you can almost see them sitting there to this day.

(See Image 27, page 83.) The strange part about being at the press site is, when something is happening and you are wondering what's going on, you cannot just "tune in" and find out, because no one outside of NASA itself knows. You see, when someone is at the press site, they ARE the source through which public gets their information. So, since we are the front line, when stuff crops up we all just sit tight and wait for NASA to let us know the status so we can pass it on to the public. The NASA folks at the press site are really super. They help as much as they can, but often we in the media sit around and speculate without them and try and figure out what is coming next.

For STS-135 I was only in the press room long enough to say hello to some of the hardcores when the meatpuppet storm began. In short order media from all over the world were squeezing into the press room or setting up shop, many doing so in assorted EZ-up tents outside. One of the hardcores looked around the room and she quietly said,

"I wish they'd all go away and just let us, who cover these things, cover it."

Then she pointed with her finger toward individuals standing nearby, as if she were able to select people and said,

"You can stay, you can stay, you can stay…"

She pointed at me and paused for a second.

"Hey," I quipped, "I was at X-Prize with you… I have cred."

"Yeah," she smirked, "you can stay."

Whew.

At recent Shuttle launches there had actually been a third category of media that remained somewhat self-isolated. They were the "Tweeters." In a good P.R. move, NASA recognized the effect that the cyber crowd could have on raising awareness of Shuttle missions. In keeping with that they began to credential persons who applied to come and simply "tweet" on social media's Twitter about being at the launch. Thus, a group who collectively knew about as much about actual spaceflight as the average Star Trek geek, ended up sitting at their computers and describing their experiences in 140 characters or less. A crowd of these tweeters were thus placed into a huge white tent with their computers. Oddly, since their greatest interest was tweeting, you hardly ever saw any of the tweeters around the press site. They all stayed in their tent with their computers.

One exception to the tweeters self isolation was when the astrovan drove past with the Shuttle crew aboard. Then the tweeters stormed from their tent in a massive geek stampede to the roadway. There they stood and waved to the van. It was actually quite a frightening sight as this rush of tweeters came out of their tent. I happened to be walking across their intended path when the STS-135 stampede took place and felt compelled to run for my life! Once the astrovan had passed, the tweeters simply and quickly funneled back into their tent to tweet about the astrovan in 140 characters or less.

No one at the press site really thought that there was much of a chance for a launch on July 8. We kept joking about being there just to cover the scrub and asking what time everyone was coming back tomorrow. The weather, however, had the last word and ended up fooling even the hardcores. As the time arrived to come out of the T-9 minute hold, the weather simply opened up into "Go conditions."

We all came out of the press building as the clock began counting beyond T-9:00 and we simply stood there waiting. Just like STS-2, 30 years earlier, as the countdown hit T-:31 seconds the clock abruptly stopped! The normal "loop" that is broadcast over the outdoor loudspeakers was fairly muted by the crowd noise, so the hold at T-:31 seconds caught everyone off guard and we heard the faint phrase "...due to a failure." One of the hardcores with a phone to his ear blurted out that GOX vent hood did not show fully retracted.

"Is there a procedure for that?" I asked aloud toward no one.

Someone nearby said "If they recycle they'll be out of the window."

Another hardcore blurted out "They'll confirm with a camera."

"They can do the hydraulic pressure too," Another of the hardcores said over my shoulder.

Then, suddenly, the count resumed. Indeed they did have a procedure for that!

In less than a half a minute the Space Shuttle ATLANTIS roared to life for the final time and lifted majestically from the pad. In all of the spectacular glory that most Americans had become so complacent with, STS-135 headed toward space. The Space Shuttle showed a great deal more grace, glory and capability than those who caused the program to end.

When it was all over the meatpuppets and their crews wrapped up their gear and left as fast as they could. The rest of us simply could not leave, not yet anyway. Personally, I hung around for nearly three hours as I found it hard to get in my car and drive off of KSC. The hardcores milled around making small talk and looking for additional launch-related tidbits to write about. No one talked much about the finality of the launch. Mostly we just hung out together as true hardcore space-buffs. When I finally could bring myself to leave I took a long look around. The pads, the MLPs, the LCC, and the VAB; all of the buildings were soon to be empty and devoid of people. These were the things that I considered. The huge press site would soon be empty as well. All of the contractors who dedicated their best years to the Space Shuttle program now would see their careers vanish like the smoke from the SRBs. This was it, this was the end. Those jobs, those careers and those people are gone and they are not coming back. Unlike STS-1, when the launch represented a new beginning and amazing things to come for this nation, STS-135 represented the opposite.

It represented the end of fantastic things and showed the direction that our so-called leaders have sent this nation toward, and that is certainly not something to be proud of.

Thus, we have the omega.

STS-135:
CAST BACK INTO "THE ERA OF LIMITS"

Driving from the press site that mournful day the message from President Reagan that was sent to the crew of STS-1 on the morning of their first launch attempt was stuck in my thoughts. It read in part,

"…You go forward today in a daring enterprise and you take the hopes and prayers of all Americans with you. Through you today we all feel as giants once again. Once again we feel the surge of pride that comes from knowing we are the first and we are the best and we are so because we are free."

Clearly it was that surge of pride that was absent from that final launch of the Space Shuttle. It had been replaced by a myopic emptiness cast upon us by self-serving politicians. I recalled the sense of pride and exhilaration that was widely felt at the end of STS-1; the moment that we all heard "Wheels stop on the COLUMBIA. Wheels stop!" The feeling we Americans had, that we had just been lifted from "the Era of Limits" declared by the politicians of the late 1970s, and that we could now lead the world into the peaceful advancement of human civilization by way of spaceflight. Inside me the 15-year-old space-buff wished that we could somehow get that feeling back. Meanwhile, the historian in me gripped the reality that such a feeling spread across a nation likely will never come back. George

W. Bush left that feeling of pride generated by the Shuttle smoldering to burn itself out and Barack Obama ground it out under his shoe as thoughtlessly as he would one of his cigarette butts. We Americans, as a people, were being cast back into the phony Era of Limits – like it, or not.

Perhaps the greatest downside of growing up with spaceflight is that it has always been there and you expect that it always will be there; not only for you, but for your children too. I joined my wife and kids en route to our vacation and we had a great time. But during one moment when we were visiting a small planetarium and looking at some Shuttle images, one of my little daughters asked,

"When is the next one Daddy?"

My answer was factual, yet it seemed cold,

"There isn't one."

Upon returning home from my vacation there was less than a week left in the flight of STS-135 and perhaps in NASA's human spaceflight program. The crew had taken up the last of the "large" materials needed for the International Space Station that could not be boosted aboard any vehicle other than the Shuttle, as well as other spare parts and supplies. EVAs that had once been the wonder of the world's TV screens were now depicted only on the Internet and were completed as if they were easy to do. That illusion was thanks to the hundreds of people and thousands of hours used to develop the skills, equipment, training, tools and EMUs that were used during every second of each EVA. The crew of ATLANTIS was involved in only one such EVA during this final mission and it was only seen on the Internet.

In fact these adventures were never easy and they never will be.

Finally, ATLANTIS came home on July 21, 2011, and

landed at KSC in the hours before dawn. Although one had the feeling that the landing had taken place under cover of darkness to spare NASA some embarrassment because most of America would not be watching at that hour, in fact, orbital mechanics dictated the time of landing. As ATLANTIS touched down on Runway 15 at KSC, it struck me that it was the same runway where I had done a touch-and-go as a student pilot 33 years earlier. Now the controllers in the tower would return to having almost nothing to do, just like back in 1978.

NASA spokespeople were all over the media on that final day of the Space Shuttle program. Over and over those of us on the outside were told, "No, no, this is not the end of our human spaceflight program." As of this writing it is a mantra that is still echoed by NASA's politically appointed "leaders" more than four years after STS-135. We were told that "commercial" is on the way and our astronauts will be flying to the ISS that way… real soon. Yet, those commercial spaceflight providers have fallen farther and farther behind as the months pass by. As of this writing they are telling us that the soonest they can get a human launched from US soil will be, at best, 2017. Yet that date now appears to be slipping into 2018. That happens to be the same time-frame that Constellation's Ares I was scheduled to do the same job when the Obama administration cancelled it in 2010 in favor of handing the whole program over to those un-tried "commercial" providers.

As we wait, NASA's astronaut office is being rapidly vacated by veteran flyers and new astronaut classes are being selected with no idea as to when or how they will get off the ground, other than riding on the Russian Soyuz at a cost of ~$70,000,000 per seat, or more. The VAB has been put up for rent and Pad 39A is being leased to SpaceX.

Staffs at both the Johnson Space Center and KSC have both been whittled down to a fraction of what they were before STS-135. In short, it sure as hell looks like STS-135 is the end of NASA's human spaceflight program.

Of course NASA managers point out that the Orion spacecraft, which did its first test flight atop a Delta IV Heavy booster on the fourth day of December, 2014, will soon fly atop the Space Launch System (SLS). Thus, fears about the USA losing its dominance in space are unfounded. Yet, in April of 2014, NASA Administrator Charlie Bolden testified before Congress that if troubles developed between Russia and the United States over International Space Station access by way of Soyuz, he would retaliate by immediately going to the president and asking that both the Orion and SLS be canceled. Yes, that is the sort of mentality that is in charge of NASA in this post-Shuttle era.

In the 24 months following STS-135, a taxidermy was performed on all of the Shuttle orbiters. They were all sent to museums to be displayed; stuffed and mounted like big-game fish on the wall of a seafood restaurant. DISCOVERY was ferried to the National Air and Space Museum's Udvar-Hazy facility atop NASA 905, the same Boeing 747 SCA that had launched the ENTERPRISE on the ALT flights in 1977. Likewise, ENDEAVOUR was ferried to the California Science Center. ENTERPRISE was sent to New York City to be placed on display at the waterfront. Then 905 itself was deployed to Houston to also be stuffed and mounted as a display. ATLANTIS was moved to the KSC Visitor Complex where she was posed in a spectacular tribute to the ability of the American people and their elected leaders to be short-sighted and wasteful.

Each Shuttle orbiter was designed to fly 100 missions, yet DISCOVERY flew just 39 missions, ENDEAVOUR flew just 25 and ATLANTIS flew just 33. COLUMBIA flew 28 missions before she was lost and CHALLENGER flew just 10 missions before she was lost as well. That means that the entire Shuttle fleet flew an average of just 27% of its designed service life. That makes you wonder two things. First, would the program have been able to be sold to the Congress if they had known that the fleet would fly just over one quarter of its designed service life and then be stuck in museums? Second, what amazing tasks could the program have done for civilization if it had been allowed to fly another quarter of the designed service life?

So it is that those of us who grew up with NASA's human spaceflight program are left to sit and ponder a bleak and unsure future. We suffer from the whiplash of suddenly going from being the undisputed leader in human space-flight to being a distant third and rapidly losing ground. Our massive spaceflight launch facilities are once again being over-grown by Florida vegetation as NASA claims a bright future is being prepared for, yet they do not have the budget to make that happen. It is strangely reminiscent of the second half of the 1970s. Indeed, as far as NASA's human spaceflight program is concerned, the political "era of limits" appears to have returned and this time it is here to stay.

My question is that although I grew up with NASA's human spaceflight, will I now grow old without it?

AFTER THE END

I was once told that you should never end a book on a bummer. Of course considering the end of the Space Shuttle program, that standard is a hard one to keep. As I write this, just over three years after the last shuttle flight, the economy along Florida's Space Coast stands heavily damaged as does that around the Johnson Space Center.

The promise of "Commercial" spaceflight providers remains little more than a promise so far as manned spaceflight is concerned, and even the premise of "Commercial" itself seems to be a myth since every time there is a Federal budget hiccup those so-called "commercial" providers cry and complain that their ability has been slowed or crippled by those missing tax dollars. Should not "commercial" be just that and thus not be neutered by thinning tax dollars? Indeed the future for United States human spaceflight looks grim.

There is, however, one hope existing out there. It consists of hundreds of thousands of wide-spread glowing embers cast widely across America. If given time and fanned a bit they may re-kindle the fires of America's human spaceflight program. They largely did not exist back when Apollo ended and seem to remain brightly glowing in spite of the short-sighted politicians— they are the teachers.

Back in the 1960s and 1970s, when I was in school, spaceflight was either uncool or too complex for the grade-school teachers to present as a part of their regular lesson plans and practically no one ever considered it as an extracurricular activity. Even my science teachers were indifferent to the subject. Today, however, things have changed. Nearly every school around the nation has at least one space-buff teaching in it. Raised in the era of the Space Shuttle, educated during a time when being a space-buff was just as cool as being a sports fan, these teachers have largely been the off-shoots of the Teacher In Space effort. And rather than being discouraged by the tragic loss of Christa McAuliffe and the CHALLENGER, they were inspired by what she stood for.

In the spring of 2013, my little daughters each joined after-school "clubs" at their elementary school; one for "Art" and one for "Gardening." After several weeks of picking them up after these "clubs" it struck me that perhaps a spaceflight club may be fun. I mentioned it to one of their teachers and she lit up. It turned out that she had been to Space Camp and had also taken a group of kids to attend Space Camp and could not wait to draw up a lesson plan for a spaceflight club. We took the idea to the principal and he too could not wait to get the project going. Soon several other teachers joined in and before we even got things going we had students begging to start.

It strikes me that we are planting the seeds of America's future in space. If our country is to recover from the political gutting of our space program it will take a new generation of kids who grow up with spaceflight; who have the imagination and the real vision for space exploration. And it will be the generation of teachers who grew up with the Space Shuttle that in turn cultivates that next generation of those who may one day find themselves growing up with spaceflight. The future of United States human spaceflight can be brightened by them and perhaps by you as well.

MASTER ALARM!

Okay, there really is nothing here about a "Master Alarm!" instead this is the part of the book where I tell you how this book came about. Normally this little chapter would be titled something really boring such as "Author's notes," or "about the author" which most readers simply skip over; I know I usually do. So now that I have suckered you in, you can take this chance to read the stuff I have written in this section. It will help you come to terms with what you just finished reading.

I was not at all someone who was inside the space program or someone who was hands-on with the hardware, or someone who designed or managed any part of the United States manned spaceflight effort. By the era of the Space Shuttle my sole contribution thus far, like millions of other Americans, went no farther than watching the family TV set in the company of my model rockets while the actual events took place far away. In the case of the Space Shuttle, however, I was lucky enough to have the pathways of my life place me close enough to observe the early Shuttle missions as well as the final mission first-hand. Thereby, I was able to scream and shout "Go baby, GO!" toward the actual event in person rather than just toward my TV screen. My only real claim here is that of being someone who is good at telling the story of that experience to of all of you who, perhaps like me, also grew up with spaceflight.

If you opened this book expecting to read a deadpan, serious-as-Gene-Kranz accounting of spaceflight, you were in the wrong place. If, however, you came here to find some lost enjoyment, have a few snickers and perhaps even see a bit of yourself, while reading some cool details about spaceflight that you may not have previously known, then this was the correct book for you. If, however, you are sitting there thinking, "Who is this guy and what business does he have writing about spaceflight?" I would advise that you stop reading right now and go directly to your nearest medical center and ask them to remove that extremely large insect from your rectal passage. Once you have had that procedure done, you may return to read this text with the rest of us who actually enjoy spaceflight.

Over the years I have encountered scores of folks who are interested in spaceflight. Yet many of them only know the Space Shuttle and many of those folks only have recall of that program post-CHALLENGER. They were either too young to pay much attention before then, or simply had yet to be born, or had spent the entire decade of the 1970s and perhaps most of the 1980s distracted by disco balls, "Dallas" and video arcades. For that reason I have composed this series of stories to give them my personal perspective growing up watching the space program. Mercury, Gemini and Apollo were covered in other volumes of mine, while this one covered the Space Shuttle.

Considering that the Shuttle program ran for just over 30 years and consisted of 135 missions, a book covering each and every mission as I saw it on TV as well as the details about the mission itself would likely drag out to the point where even the most dedicated space-buff likely would lapse into a coma. Thus I, for the most part, covered those Shuttle missions that I had witnessed first-hand. It was my hope that this will keep the reading public from slipping into a space-geek- induced trance. Yet some of us were saved by web sites such as NASAspaceflight dot com and SpaceflightNow dot com which, in the later Shuttle years, gave us every detail of every mission as it happened. As of this writing they are still doing that job.

Now, if you have read any of my other volumes of "Growing Up With Spaceflight" you are now excused from reading the rest of this text, because, A: We have lived it all together anyway, and B: The rest of this chapter is all just cut-and-paste from the earlier volumes. Hey, I am a prolific writer, but I also know when to cut-and-paste.

Being a person who sat as a pre-schooler, legs crossed, on the floor of my grandma's house and watched Alan Shepard's Freedom 7 launch; and then later sat, legs crossed on the hallway floor of Nelle Haley Elementary School along with all of the other students, and watched Gemini 3 launch on TV, I was well on my way to becoming a rabid space-buff. I think because of that I can offer an interesting perspective. For those of you who are of my same generation, I hope I can offer another angle to your own memories and perhaps spark some pleasant recall with this series of books.

A good yardstick to use in measuring public interest in the space program is the news media. Prior to wide-spread cable TV, the three major networks directed most of the public's attention toward current events. After Apollo 11, people who, sadly, were born without the aviation and aerospace gene began to lose interest in the space program, and that included the producers of national TV news. Those of us who were farther evolved than TV news producers, however, simply did our best to follow the program through any source that we could find. My parents let me stay home from school to watch the televised critical events of Apollo's 12, 13, 14, 16, and 17 as well as Skylab 1, 2 and 4. My Mom said I was learning more in those few hours than I was in school anyhow. I also tried to do my best to help those who had been born without the spaceflight gene. As a sixth grader I spent every single one of my opportunities at classroom "show-N-tell" holding a model of a Saturn V or an Apollo CSM or LEM, or even a Gemini spacecraft, in front of my class and explaining assorted aspects of the vehicle and program until my teacher, Mrs. Rosure, said "That will be enough now Wes." I never caught on to the glazed eyes of my classmates who had no idea as to what I was talking about. By the spring of 1970, my classmates would groan when it was my turn at the front of the class. Of course, they later got even with me on the dodge ball field.

In some obscure ways, I have always felt as if I had some sort of a connection with the space program; for example, I am the same age as Enos the chimp. So, I guess that relates in a strange way. Of course, he was practicing for a flight onboard an Atlas rocket at Cape Canaveral at the age of three when I was still killing Boxelder bugs with a little hammer on the side of our neighbor's garage. Yet I did not have to go through electro-shock training either. They saved that until I began flight training in 1978.

Today, I make my living as a research historian and also manage to cover space stuff as the Spaceflight Analyst for the Aero-News Network. Each time that I go to the Kennedy Space Center for a launch, get my press credentials and drive through the gate, I turn right back into that little kid who sat cross-legged in front of that old cabinet TV set and watched the launches with the same level of anticipation and thrill that a kid gets at Christmas. Standing at the press site I look at those buildings and can almost see Cronkite, Chancellor, McGee and Bergman sitting there broadcasting. This series of books is intended to bring some of that same feeling back to those of you who also grew up with spaceflight, but cannot get into the press site with me.

For those of you who were born too late to witness the days of Mercury, Gemini, Apollo and the early Space Shuttle, let this series of my books be your personal time machine. It is my hope that you will be taken back to the days of your parents, aunts and uncles and even grandparents, so that you too may capture some of the essence of what it was like to grow up with spaceflight.

Each of these stories is somewhat different from the accounts of these manned space flights that you may have read in the past. Each was assembled using sources such as my own personal tapes of the television broadcasts as well as my collection of historic video. Additionally, I used actual flight transcripts of what the astronauts said during their missions and audio records of the onboard conversations. Records of the astronaut's debriefings, oral histories and technical reports on the details of the missions were also used. Biographical books also were sourced in order to gain perspective and context for events. In some cases, however, some of these had to be discarded; it is always important to remember that memories of folks, even astronauts, and including myself, can be faulty. Also, some ghost writers are too lazy to go and source official transcripts. All dialogue contained in my books has come from either official NASA transcriptions, or from my personal word-for-word transcription of audio recordings. Lastly, I tried to root out as many little obscure and fun facts as I could about each mission. So, if this book ain't fun, you're readin' it wrong.

Some footnotes about footnotes... I hate them, thus I have never used them in any of my books. Yes, I know it's not proper and all of that rot, but this is not a technical report, nor a thesis for a Master's Degree. This is a book for pleasure reading. Footnotes break up the flow of the narrative. You will, however, find reference sources in the back of the book.

If you are someone who worships at the "AP Style Guide" you will find me to be a heretic. I write in a conversational style. Again... this is not a technical report, nor a thesis for a Master's Degree. This is a book for pleasure reading. So, forgive my editors who have been forced to play by my rules here- it is my choice and they were dragged kicking and screaming into my style of writing- they'll work it out in therapy someday, you'll see.

Also, I reserve the right to be wrong. No one can be 100% correct all of the time. And for those of you who think that you know better, perhaps you do, but I thus invoke author's privilege. "What is that?" you may ask. Well, if you are going to spout off that I am, "all wrong" and cite Wikipedia, or some guy you talked to once, as a source, I would retort; "fine, when your book comes out on this subject, we will compare our works and talk." And when you tell me that you do not have a book coming out, I will then reply, "Exactly."

Finally, I am NOT any sort of an "expert" on the subject of spaceflight and I make no claim to be such. Rather, I am a professional writer, an author, a scribe, someone who can assemble facts into a story that is interesting and fun to read. You can thus correctly conclude that I am not an engineer either. If, by reading this book you learned something new and smiled and snicker at least once, then I have done my job.

SOURCES

Space Shuttle Orbiter Approach and Landing Tests- Final Evaluation Report; NASA, JSC 13864, February 1978

"1981-1999 Space Shuttle Mission Chronology" NASA, U.S. Government Printing Office: 2000- 633010/26704

"X-15 The NASA Mission Reports" Robert Godwin

"Space Shuttle STS 1-5 – The NASA Mission Reports" Robert Godwin

"Enterprise" Jerry Grey

"The Space Shuttle" Frank Ross Jr.

"Exploring Tomorrow In Space" Thomas W. Becker

"Space-Liner" William Stockton and John Noble Wilford

"Space Shuttle, the History of the National Space Transportation System." Dennis R. Jenkins

"Space Shuttle Decision, 1965-1972" T.A. Heppenheimer

"Live TV From Orbit" Dwight Steven-Boniecki

"Flying Without Wings" Milt Thompson and Curtis Peebles

"Wingless Flight" R. Dale Reed and Darlene Lister

"From Runway to Orbit" Kennith W. Illiff and Curtis Peebles

"To Orbit and Back" Davide Sivolella

"Forever Young" John W. Young and James R. Hansen

Peter W. Merlin, "Free Enterprise: Contributions of the Approach and Landing Test (ALT) Program to the Development of the Space Shuttle Orbiter," Paper No. AIAA-2006-7467 (Presented at American Institute of Aeronautics and Astronautics)

"50 Years Of Rockets & Spacecraft In The Rocket City" NASA-MSFC Retiree Association

A Tow Concept For The Space Shuttle Orbiter Approach And Landing Test, NASA-TM-X-73972, August 24, 1976

Space Shuttle Program Orbiter Approach & Landing Test, Pre-ALT Report, NASA, February 1977

Orbiter Flight Series Press Kit, NASA- N77-16095

Orbiter Flight Series Press Kit, NASA- N77-81091

Orbiter Flight Series Press Kit, NASA- N77-224

Orbiter Flight Series Press Kit, NASA- N77-10226

Orbiter Flight Series Press Kit, NASA- N77-233

Space Shuttle Orbiter Approach And Landing Test, Final Evaluation Report, NASA, JSC-13864

Orbiter/Shuttle Carrier Aircraft Separation, NASA Technical Memorandum- TM-58223

Shuttle Performance: Lessons Learned, NASA Conference Publication 2283, March 8-10, 1983

MSFC Space Shuttle Program; Development, Assembly and Testing Major Events (1969-April 1981) NASA-CR-184,013, August 15, 1989

STS-1 Technical Crew Debrief, NASA, April, 1981

STS-1 First Space Shuttle Mission Press Kit, April 1981

STS-2 Orbiter Mission Report, NASA, February 1982

STS-2 Second Space Shuttle Mission Press Kit, September 1981

STS-3 Orbiter Mission Report, NASA, June 1982

STS-3 Third Space Shuttle Mission Press Kit, March 1982

STS-4 Orbiter Mission Report, NASA, September 1982

STS-5 Press Information, November 1982

STS-5 Space Shuttle Program Mission Report, December 1982

STS-6 Press Information, Rockwell, March 1983

STS-7 Press Information, Rockwell, June 1983

STS-8 Press Information, Rockwell, August 1983

STS-8 National Space Transportation System Program Mission Report, NASA, JSC-19278, October 1983

STS-8 Press Information, Rockwell, November 1983

STS-9 Orbital Workshop Spacelab to Fly on Ninth Shuttle

Mission, NASA-TM-85497, October 1983

STS-41B Press Kit, NASA, Release No. 84-4, February 1984

STS-61A Press Kit, NASA, Release No. 85-145, August 1985

Karol J. "Bo" Bobko, Oral History Transcript, NASA, February 12, 2002

Vance D. Brand, Oral History Transcript, NASA, April 25, 2000, April 12, 2002

Joe H. Engle, Oral History Transcript, NASA, June 3, 2004

Henry W. Hartsfield

Jack R. Lousma, Oral History Transcript, NASA, March 7, 2001, March 15, 2010, Oral History Transcript, NASA, June 12 and 15, 2001

T. K. Mattingly, Oral History Transcript, NASA, November 6, 2001, April 22, 2002

Richard H. Truly, Oral History Transcript, NASA, June 16, 2003

"Space Shuttle Seating" Spaceflight magazine, April, 1971

"A Schedule for the Space Shuttle" David Baker, Spaceflight magazine, December, 1971

"Space Shuttle- An Economic Appraisal" David Baker Spaceflight magazine, February, 1972

"Space Shuttle Main Engine" Spaceflight magazine, February, 1972

"The Space Shuttle: Concept and Implications" D.j. Farrar Spaceflight magazine, March, 1972

"The Space Shuttle" Spaceflight magazine, April, 1972

"Space Shuttle: Crisis and Decision" David Dooling Jr. Spaceflight magazine, July, 1972

"Europe and Post-Apollo" Kenneth W. Gatland, Spaceflight magazine, September, 1972

"Free Enterprise: Contributions of the Approach and

Landing Test (ALT) Program to the Development of the Space Shuttle Orbiter," Peter W. Merlin, Analytical Services and Materials, Inc., NASA Dryden Flight Research Center (Astronautics Space Conference, San Jose, CA, September 21, 2006)

Author's conversations with Jack Lousma aboard c.COLUMBUS, October 2001

Author's conversation with Bob Cabana, March 1, 2014

Wayne Hale's Blog, "After Ten Years, Too Little, Too Late" 1/12/2013

Author's spaceflight audio tape and video collection

Thanks to Miles O'Brien for proof-reading the STS-125 chapter and saving my beacon... err... I mean bacon.

AUTHOR ACKNOWLEDGEMENTS

This is normally the section where I deliver thanks to libraries, researchers and private collectors, etc. Most of those who need acknowledgement will actually be found in the text or bibliography, so here I am going to place thanks upon those who are not in the text. There are a few ultra-important folks without whom I would never have produced this series of e-books. When I first decided to stick my toe into the e-book world I did some forum reading and saw how many newbie e-authors were bashing their brains over one critical area: formatting. So I contacted my long-time friend, fellow professional pilot and author as well as ERAU alumnus, Mark Berry. He had already done some e-books and when asked he put me in contact with Kristina Blank Makansi, the editor and publisher at Blank Slate Press (blankslatepress.com) and founder of Blank Slate Author Services. With her guidance I discovered just how sheltered my life has been while working in print and how much my print publisher has done that I took for granted. She taught me about things such as proper photo DPI, bar codes, ISBNs and countless other areas upon which I would have stumbled. Joining Kristina in the effort was her daughter Elena who took on the task of formatting the interior and placing photos in the book. Together they form a professional team that was instrumental in bringing this book and those that will follow, into reality. I thank them. Finally I'd like to acknowledge Emily Carney, who owns and operates the FaceBook "Space Hipsters" site and a darned good spaceflight writer as well. She did not have a hand in making this book, but she really likes it when authors acknowledge her. And I'm in hope that this acknowledgement will inspire her to take a selfie with this book next to her ear and post it on her site. Thus, although she may not have had a hand in making the book, she will certainly have a hand in selling it.

ABOUT THE AUTHOR

Author Wes Oleszewski was born and raised in mid-Michigan and spent most of his life with an eye turned toward the space, flight and spaceflight. Since 1990 he has authored eighteen books on the subject of Great Lakes maritime history. Now he has turned his attention toward spaceflight.

Noted for his meticulous research, Oleszewski has a knack for weeding out the greatest of details from the most obscure events and then weaving those facts into the historical narratives which are his stories. His tales of actual events are real enough to thrill any reader while every story is technically correct and highly educational. Oleszewski feels that the only way to teach history in this age of computer and video games is through "narrative." The final product of his efforts are captivating books that can be comfortably read and enjoyed by everyone from the eldest grandmother to the grade-school kid and future pilot or historian.

Born on the east side of Saginaw, Michigan in 1957, Wes Oleszewski attended public school in that city through grade nine, when his family moved to the town of Freeland, Michigan. In 1976 he graduated from Freeland High School and a year later entered the Embry-Riddle Aeronautical University in Daytona, Florida. Working his way through college by way of his own earned income,

Oleszewski graduated in 1987 with a commercial pilot's certificate, "multi-engine and instrument airplane" ratings as well as a B.S. Degree in Aeronautical Science. He has pursued a career as a professional pilot as well as one as an author. He holds an A.T.P. certificate and has twice been elevated to the position of Captain. To date has logged three logbooks of flight time most of which is in airline category and jet aircraft. Recently he gave up the life of a professional aviator and now enjoys his job as a professional writer.

For more excitement, visit Wes's websites:
www.klydemorris.com
www.gwsbooks.blogspot.com

Made in the USA
Charleston, SC
07 December 2015